Poetry skills

Learning language through poetry

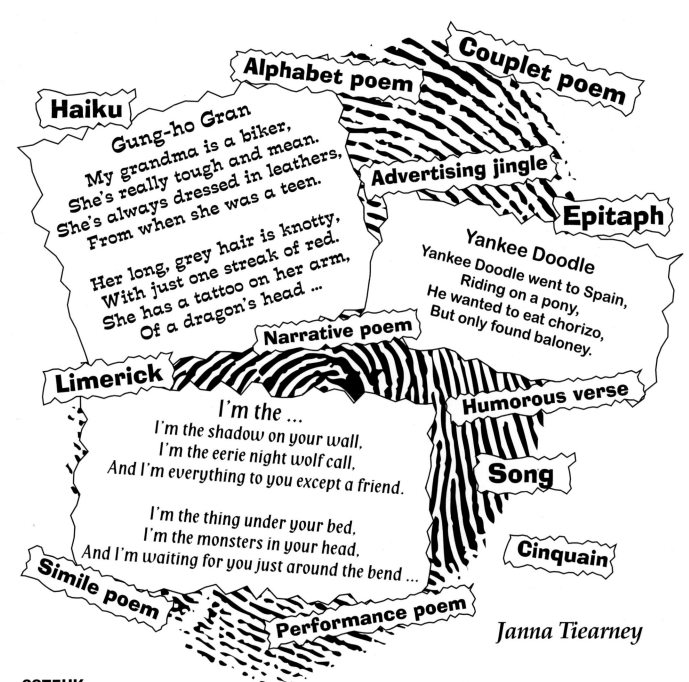

Haiku

Alphabet poem

Couplet poem

Gung-ho Gran
My grandma is a biker,
She's really tough and mean.
She's always dressed in leathers,
From when she was a teen.

Her long, grey hair is knotty,
With just one streak of red.
She has a tattoo on her arm,
Of a dragon's head ...

Advertising jingle

Epitaph

Yankee Doodle
Yankee Doodle went to Spain,
Riding on a pony,
He wanted to eat chorizo,
But only found baloney.

Narrative poem

Limerick

Humorous verse

I'm the ...
I'm the shadow on your wall,
I'm the eerie night wolf call,
And I'm everything to you except a friend.

I'm the thing under your bed,
I'm the monsters in your head,
And I'm waiting for you just around the bend ...

Song

Cinquain

Simile poem

Performance poem

Janna Tiearney

6275UK

73/7

POETRY SKILLS
(Middle)

Published by Prim-Ed Publishing 2007
Copyright© Janna Tiearney 2006
ISBN 978-1-84654-064-6
PR–6275

Additional titles available in this series:
POETRY SKILLS *(Lower)*
POETRY SKILLS *(Upper)*

Internet websites

In some cases, websites or specific URLs may be recommended. While these are checked and rechecked at the time of publication, the publisher has no control over any subsequent changes which may be made to webpages. It is *strongly* recommended that the class teacher checks *all* URLs before allowing pupils to access them.

View all pages online

Website: www.prim-ed.com

Email: sales@prim-ed.com

Foreword

Poetry skills is a fun and innovative series, designed to help pupils learn and practise the English language. It is not a series purely to teach poetry, but rather a means to study language through the medium of poetry.

With the ever-increasing burden placed on them, teachers will find these lessons practical and enjoyable, with structured lessons to include all key areas of the curriculum, and to develop all the necessary skills.

Poetry is a child-friendly way to approach the teaching of language through reading, listening to and writing poetry, which will not only benefit the pupil's language awareness but also increase his/her confidence.

There is a selection of humorous and relevant poems on familiar topics. Many different types of poems have been included, which will give pupils the opportunity to experience and explore different types of text and settings. Pupils enjoy poems with rhythm and rhyme and many of the included poems contain these elements.

Since poetry requires a certain amount of fluency, pupil's reading skills will be developed, in a more exciting and interesting way, through reading, practising, reciting and learning poetry. Comprehension skills will also be enhanced.

The shorter texts and flexibility of lessons make this book suitable for both mainstream and special needs pupils.

The shorter written tasks will prove less daunting and will enable pupils to complete work in which all their learned skills will be utilised.

Through studying poetry, pupils will be given the chance to explore feelings—their own and the feelings of others—and will, in turn, be able to express their own feelings on a range of subjects, while drawing on their own personal experiences and their imagination.

A poem is not a thing we see, but rather a light by which we may see ... and what we see is life.

Robert Penn Warren

The books in this series are:

Poetry skills – Lower (5–7 years)

Poetry skills – Middle (7–9 years)

Poetry skills – Upper (9–11+ years)

Curriculum links

Country	Subject	Level	Objectives
England	Literacy	Year 3	• Prepare poems for performance, identifying appropriate expression, tone, volume and use of voices. • Use drama strategies to explore stories. • Identify the main points of a text. • Identify how different texts are organised. • Explore how different texts appeal to readers. • Share and compare reasons for reading preferences. • Use beginning, middle and end to write narratives.
		Year 4	• Offer reasons and evidence for their views. • Comment constructively on performances. • Read genres extensively. • Show imagination through use of language.
Northern Ireland	Language and literacy	KS 2	• Listen and respond to a range of poetry. • Improvise a scene based on experience, imagination and literature. • Read aloud, inflecting appropriately. • Use appropriate quality of speech and voice and speak audibly. • Retell and interpret stories. • Read and understand a range of texts. • Take part in shared and paired reading experiences. • Retell, reread and act out familiar poems. • Explore familiar stories and other simple texts using drama and discussion. • Read aloud from familiar texts. • Discuss and interpret texts. • Justify their responses logically, by inference, deduction or reference to evidence within the text. • Extend their range of reading and develop their own preferences. • Write creatively using a variety of poetry forms. • Experiment with rhymes, rhythms and verse structure. • Experiment with poetic forms. • Undertake shared, guided, modelled and independent writing. • Use imagination to express thoughts, feelings and opinions in written form. • Write creatively using imaginative vocabulary. • Write for a variety of purposes.
Scotland	English	Level C	• Listen carefully to obtain relevant information and answer questions. • Respond to texts using discussion and drama. • Give personal responses to texts in writing. • Recognise development of verse, mood, rhythm and comparison in poems. • Bring an awareness of self and their emotions and attitudes to texts. • Compare and contrast own experiences with texts. • Develop awareness of audience and listeners' needs. • Explore effects of rhythm and verse length. • Identify main ideas of texts through literal and inferential responses. • Recognise differences between poems; e.g. narrative and description. • Develop skills of reading aloud. • Develop their imaginative writing. • Read poetry aloud to aid poetry writing.
Wales	English	KS 2	• Read aloud, tell and enact poems. • Participate in a wide range of drama activities. • Listen carefully and recall important features of a reading. • Participate in independent and shared reading of texts. • Read a wide range of literature, including modern poetry. • Consider in detail what they read and respond imaginatively. • Use inference, deduction and prediction to evaluate the texts they read. • Write in response to a wide range of stimuli, including poems. • Use the characteristics of different kinds of writing. • Write in forms that include imaginative writing. • Plan, draft and improve their work. • Discuss and evaluate their own and others' writing. • Develop their ability to organise and structure their writing in a variety of ways, using their experience of poetry.

Contents

Teachers notes

Teachers page

A teachers page accompanies each pupil worksheet. It provides the following information:

Objective/Activities covered

The activity objective and a list of activities are included for easy reference.

Background information for each activity is included for the teacher.

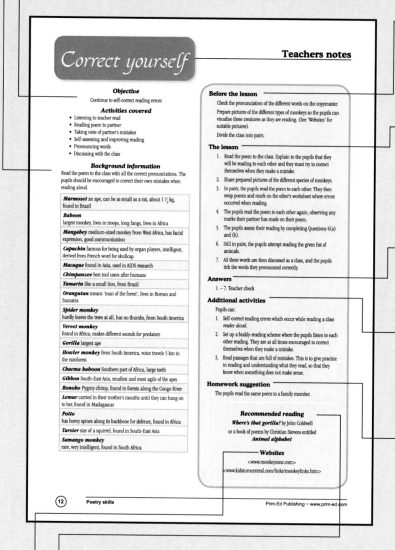

Before the lesson – the teacher is made aware of what needs to be done before the lesson. Some materials and tasks are required for the lesson to be conducted; others are suggestions that will enrich the lesson.

The lesson – gives suggested step-by-step instructions for using the worksheet. Often, a list of words contained in a poem that may require clarification is included, as it is important that all words in a poem are understood by the pupils.

Answers – for the activities are included. Some answers will need a teacher check, while others may vary depending on personal experiences, opinions or feelings.

Additional activities – can be used to further develop the objective of the worksheet. These activities provide ideas to consolidate and clarify the concepts and skills taught in the lesson.

Homework suggestions – are included on many teachers pages. The aim of the suggested homework is to provide a link between school and home; therefore, the work often involves elements of the lesson being shared or practised with a family member.

Recommended reading – provides further examples of the type of poetry being studied. Poetry books should be available in the classroom and school library for the pupils to access. It is important for pupils to read, and have read to them, poetry by different authors, as the poems on the worksheets have all been written by the same author.

Websites – are suggested on many pages to help teachers and/or pupils find other examples of poetry. Websites were current and appropriate at the time of printing; however, teachers should check before allowing the pupils to use them and refer to their school's Internet policy.

Teachers notes

Pupil page

Poem

A poem, usually on a familiar topic, is found on each pupil page. Many different types of poems have been included to give the pupils the opportunity to experience and explore a variety of texts and settings and to motivate them. Poetry forms used include concrete poetry, haiku, cinquain, list, clerihew, sense, sausage, chant and tongue twister. Pupils enjoy rhyming poems with humour and a strong rhythm, and many of the poems in this book contain these elements. The importance of rhyme and rhythm could be emphasised by having the pupils beat out their rhythm by clapping or using musical instruments.

- Through the lesson, the pupils will learn that poetry comes in a variety of forms, but always expresses important personal feelings and gives a unique insight into the mind of the creator.

- If the poem is to be read aloud, the teacher should use much expression to promote enthusiasm, as some pupils have a negative view of poetry.

Correct yourself

If you make a mistake when you are reading, do not worry! The important thing is to correct yourself and carry on.

❶ Listen to the teacher read this poem:

❷ Read the poem to a partner.

❸ Swap poems and underline where your partner is going wrong. (Make sure your partner corrects his/her own mistakes.)

❹ Read the poem to each other again, being careful where it is underlined.

(a) How many mistakes did you make this time? ☐

(b) How many mistakes did you correct yourself? ☐

❺ Read the poem together.

❻ Still in your pairs, try pronouncing these animal names.

(a) orangutan .... ☐
(b) spider monkey .... ☐
(c) vervet monkey .... ☐
(d) gorilla .... ☐
(e) howler monkey .... ☐
(f) chacma baboon .... ☐
(g) gibbon .... ☐
(h) bonobo .... ☐
(i) lemur .... ☐
(j) potto .... ☐
(k) tarsier .... ☐
(l) samango monkey .... ☐

Thank goodness!

I *am* glad I am not a monkey,
A marmoset or a baboon,
I'd have to eat insects for breakfast,
And dine on bananas at noon!

I *am* glad I am not a monkey,
A mangabey or capuchin,
I'd have to hang onto my mother,
And scrounge for snacks in the bin!

I *am* glad I am not a monkey,
A macaque or a chimpanzee,
I'd have to hang upside down by my tail,
And spend my life in a tree!

I *am* glad I am not a monkey,
Or a tamarin all in a flap,
I'd have to nibble my sister's fleas,
I am glad that I am a chap!

A male orangutan makes burping noises to scare off other males!

❼ Discuss the difficult words with your teacher and the class. Tick them if you got the pronunciation right.

Prim-Ed Publishing ~ www.prim-ed.com — Poetry skills ⑬

Activities

- In the activities, the pupils will be given the chance to explore and express feelings (their own and those of others) on a range of subjects, while drawing on their own experiences and imagination.

- The activity may:
  - introduce or reinforce a topic
  - allow for expression of thoughts, feelings and moods
  - allow for discussion of personal opinions and interpretations of a poem
  - promote a love of words.

- Discussion is a vital part of lessons and may include class, group or pair work. This will give the pupils the opportunity to share their efforts and experiences together.

- Pupils are encouraged on many of the worksheets to check or self-assess their work.

- Interesting facts, jokes or common sayings have been included on many of the worksheets. Teachers could use these as a springboard for further discussion or writing tasks.

Further ideas

- It is suggested that the pupils keep a 'Poetry portfolio'. This will allow the teacher to quickly see what worksheets have been covered.

- The pupils' poetry efforts should be praised and their work displayed on a regular basis in the classroom, around the school, in the school newspaper or in a class anthology. This should occur in an atmosphere where criticism is both positive and constructive, encouraging the pupils to be innovative and to take risks with their writing.

Listen to the teacher

Objective

Experience the teacher's use of challenging vocabulary and sentence structure

Activities covered

- Listening to teacher
- Writing meanings
- Discussing answers with class
- Reading poem
- Drawing

Background information

The teacher in the classroom is the one to set the standards of correct language usage. If pupils use slang, or use words in an incorrect context, the teacher should be pointing out mistakes and explaining the correct way. It is vital therefore that teachers are speaking correctly. Teachers should also introduce harder words every now and then to keep pupils questioning and exploring. All new words and phrases should be written in the pupil's word books.

Before the lesson

Prepare a list of sentences which make use of the words in Question 2. (See answers for an example).

The lesson

1. Read the poem to the class, using much expression. Words are not discussed at this point.
2. Read aloud the sentences containing the list of words, from Question 2. (Some examples of suitable sentences are provided in the answer section.)
3. The pupils complete Question 2, guessing if they do not know.
4. Discuss all the words as a class.
5. Re-read the poem.
6. Discuss the poem as a whole. The pupils can talk a little about healthy eating. Use more challenging words during this discussion, such as 'nutritious', 'energy', 'physical' or any other words to do with healthy living.
7. The pupils draw a healthy breakfast to complete Question 5.

Answers

1. Teacher check
2. Answers will vary but should be similar to the following:
   - (a) get wrong idea of something
   - (b) I am in trouble
   - (c) fatty substance found in body tissue
   - (d) shows different food groups
   - (e) make or become hot enough to bubble and give off steam
   - (f) cook under grill/part of oven where heat is at top
   - (g) tubes carrying blood from heart
   - (h) cook with steam

   Examples of sentences:
   - (a) *My teacher misunderstood me and thought I had not done my homework.*
   - (b) *'My goose is fried! I forgot to bring the washing in and it's pouring with rain!'*
   - (c) *If you have high cholesterol it could lead to a heart attack.*
   - (d) *The food pyramid shows we need to eat lots of vegetables.*
   - (e) *Boil that delicious cabbage for five minutes.*
   - (f) *Place the pasta under the grill to melt the cheese.*
   - (g) *Arteries carry blood from your heart.*
   - (h) *Please steam those vegetables in the microwave.*

3. – 5. Teacher check

Additional activities

Pupils can:

1. Tell stories, recite poems and read short stories or newspaper articles to the class.
2. Repeat a sentence, using new and challenging words.

Homework suggestion

Have the pupils look at food labels, especially fat content, and discuss their findings with the class the following day. During the discussion, pupils should be encouraged to use new words.

Recommended reading

What teachers wear in bed by Brian Moses

Stinkerman by David Harmer

Calling all teachers by Marian Swinger.

(Or any poems that make use of more challenging words.)

1 Listen to the teacher read this poem.

> ### Misunderstood
>
> *'Oh, no!' said Tom, 'My goose is fried!'*
>
> *'Oh, don't say that!' the teacher cried.*
>
> *'Don't you know fried food is bad?*
>
> *Haven't you heard of cholesterol, lad?*
>
> *The food pyramid does clearly show*
>
> *We must keep fat intake low!*
>
> *Otherwise, you'll get obese,*
>
> *And all because of your fried geese!*
>
> *Now, boy, you must use the grill*
>
> *So your arteries don't feel ill!*
>
> *You can bake and steam and boil,*
>
> *And always use pure olive oil!*
>
> *I hope you've taken all this in*
>
> *Fatty foods go in the bin!'*
>
> *'No, Miss, I really get you not,*
>
> *It's just my homework I forgot.'*

3 Discuss your answers with the class.

4 Read the poem again!

5 Draw a healthy breakfast in the box.

2 Listen to the teacher read some sentences. Write what you think each word or phrase means below. Guess if you do not know.

(a) misunderstood

_____

_____

(b) My goose is fried

_____

_____

(c) cholesterol

_____

(d) food pyramid

_____

(e) boil

_____

(f) grill

_____

(g) arteries

_____

(h) steam

_____

> We should eat six servings of fruit and vegetables every day.

Objective

Become increasingly aware of the importance of tone of voice in communicating with others

Activities covered

- Reading a poem as a class
- Discussing poem
- Reading poem aloud, with a partner, taking different roles
- Identifying parts of a poem
- Reading sentences using different tones
- Writing true or false
- Identifying tone

Background information

Pupils must be made aware that they communicate their feelings through their tone of voice and body language. They should get much practice in reading aloud and become used to reading clearly, with expression, correct pronunciation and correct tone of voice.

Before the lesson

Divide the class into pairs. Have a list placed somewhere in the classroom or on the board to remind pupils what they need to be thinking about when they are reading.

The lesson

1. Ask pupils to show different facial expressions and various forms of body language at the start of the lesson.
2. Read the poem with the class. Tell the pupils this lesson focuses on tone of voice using correct expression; e.g. Jake's family members would be angry, Jake would be unaware that he is being rude etc.
3. Discuss the poem as a class including talking about the terms 'stepping over the line', 'fake' and 'committed a crime' and suitable expression for the poem.
4. In pairs, the pupils read the poem, each taking different roles. They must concentrate on how they are reading the poem and how they are using their body language.
5. The pupils complete Question 4.
6. Still in pairs, the pupils read the given sentences using different tones of voice.
7. The pupils complete Questions 6 and 7.

Answers

1. – 5. Teacher check
6. (a) true   (b) false   (c) true
7. Teacher check

Additional activities

Pupils can:

1. Read other poems, using correct expression and body language.
2. Play a game where they mime and others must guess what they are feeling.
3. Put together a short play, using no words at all, only gesture and movement.
4. In groups, recite poems, concentrating on clarity and pronunciation of words.

Homework suggestion

The pupils concentrate on using only a kind and pleasant tone at home, and report back about their experience.

Recommended reading

You're not going out like that
by Paul Cookson and David Harmer

Just look at yourself by Janis Priestley

Waiting for the tone by Brian Patten

Said the boy to the dinosaur
by Colin McNaughton

I don't be-leaf you by Polly Peters

1 Read this poem as a class.

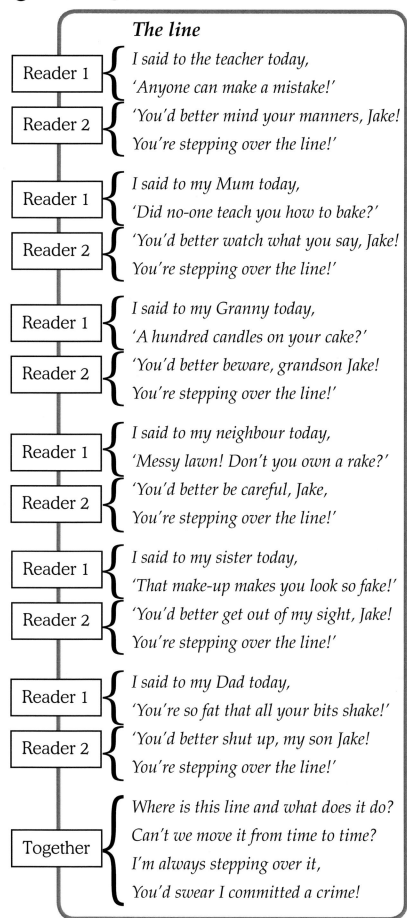

The line

Reader 1
I said to the teacher today,
'Anyone can make a mistake!'

Reader 2
'You'd better mind your manners, Jake!
You're stepping over the line!'

Reader 1
I said to my Mum today,
'Did no-one teach you how to bake?'

Reader 2
'You'd better watch what you say, Jake!
You're stepping over the line!'

Reader 1
I said to my Granny today,
'A hundred candles on your cake?'

Reader 2
'You'd better beware, grandson Jake!
You're stepping over the line!'

Reader 1
I said to my neighbour today,
'Messy lawn! Don't you own a rake?'

Reader 2
'You'd better be careful, Jake,
You're stepping over the line!'

Reader 1
I said to my sister today,
'That make-up makes you look so fake!'

Reader 2
'You'd better get out of my sight, Jake!
You're stepping over the line!'

Reader 1
I said to my Dad today,
'You're so fat that all your bits shake!'

Reader 2
'You'd better shut up, my son Jake!
You're stepping over the line!'

Together
Where is this line and what does it do?
Can't we move it from time to time?
I'm always stepping over it,
You'd swear I committed a crime!

2 Discuss the poem with the class.

3 Find a partner. One person will play Jake and the other person will play the other characters. Read the poem together using the correct tone of voice.

4 Tick on the poem where you think Jake was stepping over the line.

5 Still in pairs, say these sentences using the following tones.

happy, sad, bored, angry, grumpy

(a) I will go to bed now.

(b) Jack is coming to visit me.

6 Write true or false.
(a) You should always speak in a polite tone.

_____

(b) Your tone of voice cannot change.

_____

(c) Your tone of voice can tell others how you are feeling.

_____

7 How does your teacher's tone of voice sound today?

_____

Mime it

Objective

Use mime to convey ideas, reactions, emotions, desires and attitudes

Activities covered

- Reading a poem as a group
- Answering questions
- Adding actions to a poem
- Practising mime
- Performing mime
- Assessing mime
- Writing a sentence

Background information

The pupils act out a poem in this lesson, using no words at all, only actions. It could be explained to the pupils that their actions might have to be exaggerated to get the message across. Body language and facial expressions are important too as they will give clues about the feelings. In the poem, the child goes through various emotions and this should be conveyed in the pupils' mimes.

Before the lesson

Divide the class into groups.

The lesson

1. Read the poem to the class, using different expressions as the child in the poem goes through different emotions. Remind the pupils what mime is by reading the information at the top of the page.
2. Discuss the poem with the class mentioning harder words such as 'scrambles', 'unsteady', 'outa', 'barely', 'flailing' and 'meek'.
3. The pupils read the poem together in their groups.
4. The pupils consider the feelings of the boy in the poem to complete Question 2.
5. The pupils decide how they will act out the poem as a group. One person in the group should be the reader while others perform the actions. The pupils can write on the poem what they are doing. Give the pupils some time to practise their mimes.
6. The pupils perform their mime for the class and then assess their performance by completing Question 5.
7. The pupils describe how it feels to be on a trampoline to complete Question 6. This should be a full sentence.

Answers

1. Teacher check
2. (a) He felt nervous and unsure.   (b) He felt happy and free.
3. – 6. Teacher check

Additional activity

Pupils can:

Mime parts of their class reader, stories they have written themselves, problems they may have, special events, stories in history, different feelings or emotions, TV or film titles, reactions, characters in stories, animals etc.

Recommended reading
(to mime)

The itch by Michael Rosen

No talking!

To mime is to add actions to a story or poem, without using any words.

Take a jump

At first he scrambles on,
his legs are quite unsteady.
I say 'Go on - take a jump!'
He says, 'When I'm ready!'

He unfolds himself and stands,
and takes a little hop.
He says, 'Get me outa here,
I just want to stop!'

He takes a few tiny jumps,
his feet barely leave the ground.
'Come on', I say but his lips are tight,
he doesn't make a sound.

But slowly the jumps get stronger,
and out escapes a laugh.
'Hey, Mum, can you see me?
I'm as tall as a giraffe!'

The jumps get bigger and mightier.
He even starts to shriek.
Arms and legs flailing about,
where was that boy so meek?

'Be careful!' I said and 'Don't you fall!'
He was the free-est I'd ever seen.
But he was in another world
on his brand new trampoline.

Have you heard of the expression: 'Take a jump!'?

❶ Read the poem as a group.

❷ (a) How did the boy feel at the beginning of the poem?

_____

(b) How did the boy feel at the end of the poem?

_____

❸ Decide as a group how you will mime this poem. You can all do the same actions or you can all do different actions. One person should be the reader. Show the boy's different feelings. Write your actions on the poem.

❹ Practise your mime a few times, then perform it for the class, while one person reads.

❺ Give your performance a star rating.

❻ How does it feel to jump on a trampoline? Write a full sentence.

_____

_____

_____

_____

What season is it when you are on a trampoline?

Spring time!

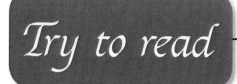

Try to read

Objective
Use more than one strategy when reading unfamiliar text

Activities covered
- Reading a poem containing difficult words
- Breaking up difficult words into parts
- Finding words that are similar
- Discussing a poem
- Finding and reading a difficult word

Background information
The words in the given poem are purposely difficult to give pupils the opportunity to try out different strategies when trying to read a word. Strategies could include breaking the word up into readable syllables, recognising words as being similar to other words that they already know or finding letter patterns or strings.

Before the lesson
Prepare some examples of difficult words to share with the class. An example of how different strategies can be used should be written on the board. (See 'Websites'). The pupils will require dictionaries.

The lesson
1. Write examples of difficult words on the board, using different strategies to read each one. Examples can be left on the board.
2. The pupils attempt to read the poem on their own, using different strategies. Discuss the meanings of words with the pupils without actually saying the words.
3. The pupils break up the words into parts to answer Question 2.
4. The pupils write words they know that are similar to the given words. Explain that words can be similar without having to rhyme to answer Question 3. Even if words do not have the same sound group, they can be similar.
5. Discuss the poem as a class, as well as the answers to Questions 2 and 3.
6. Practise saying all the difficult words as a class then read the poem again.
7. The pupils look for a difficult word in the dictionary. They then write the word, break it up, write a similar word and read the word to answer Question 4.

Answers
1. Teacher check
2. (a) ka/ki/dro/sis (b) ker/fuff/le (c) knack/ish (d) kill/cow
   (e) keck/le (f) kipp/age (g) knub/ble
3. Answers will vary but may include the following:
   (a) keck – deck, neck, peck, wreck, check, kick
   (b) shout, snout, knee (c) speckle, pickle
   (d) rash, sash, mash (e) stubble, rubble, knight
4. Teacher check

Additional activities
Pupils can:
1. Apply the same strategies for reading difficult words they used on the copymaster when reading the class reading book aloud or reading words in other learning areas.
2. Apply the learned strategies to read given groups of difficult words.

Homework suggestion
The pupils choose five difficult words from the poem and write five sentences. They read these to a family member who has to guess the meaning of the word.

Recommended reading
Nine reasons for hating children
by Fred Sedgwick

Websites
<www.worldwidewords.org/weirdwords>
<http://phrontistery.info>
(for teachers)

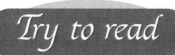

When trying to read a difficult word, break it into smaller parts.
You can also ask yourself if it looks similar to another word you know.

1 Read this poem on your own. (Beware! Some words are difficult!)

> **Do not give up!**

K is for kids

Kinchins are a wonderful bunch,
But mathematics makes them keck,
They could suffer from kakidrosis,
And cause a kerfuffle or wreck.

You'll find them awfully knackish,
And a killcow is not rare,
But please don't ever knout them,
Or keckle them to the chair.

For breakfast they will not eat kasha,
For dinner, kohlrabi won't do,
And if ever they show signs of kippage,
Don't knubble them till they're blue!

Word meanings:

Kinchin – a child

Keck – to feel disgust

Kakidrosis – body odour

Kerfuffle – disorder

Kasha – porridge or gruel-like dish made from crushed buckwheat

Kohlrabi – variety of cabbage

Kippage – state of displeasure or anger

Knubble – beat with fists

Knackish – cunning, crafty

Killcow – bully

> **Kids should be seen and not heard! Do you agree?**

Knout – flog

Keckle – to protect by binding with rope

2 Break up these words; e.g. kin/chin

(a) kakidrosis _____

(b) kerfuffle _____

(c) knackish _____

(d) killcow _____

(e) keckle _____

(f) kippage _____

(g) knubble _____

3 Write a word you know that sounds similar to these.

(a) keck – _____

(b) knout – _____

(c) keckle – _____

(d) kasha – _____

(e) knubble – _____

4 Find a difficult word in the dictionary.

(a) Write it.

_____

(b) Break it up.

_____

(c) Write a similar word:

_____

(d) Can you read it? ☐ Yes ☐ No

Objective

Identify unfamiliar words by reference to prefixes

Activities covered

- Reading poem
- Underlining 'un' words
- Writing words where 'un' makes opposites
- Recognising opposite words

Background information

This lesson introduces the pupils to prefixes. Pupils should be able to use the strategy of identifying unfamiliar words by looking at word parts. Pupils could build up a list of prefixes and suffixes during the year and these can be displayed. In this lesson, the word 'prefix' can be used and explained so that the pupils become familiar with it.

Before the lesson

Prepare a list of other 'un' words or another example of a prefix.

The lesson

1. Discuss prefixes and share some examples with the class; e.g. 'in' – incomplete, incorrect, inedible, inactive. Note: the prefix 'in' will not always make the word opposite; e.g. invite, injure etc.

2. Read the poem as a class.

3. The pupils underline the words that start with 'un' to complete Question 2.

4. The pupils write words where 'un' makes each word opposite in meaning to complete Question 3.

5. The pupils circle the words where 'un' makes a word opposite in meaning to complete Question 4.

6. The pupils make each word opposite by adding 'un' to complete Question 5.

Answers

1. Teacher check

2. uninvited, uniform, unbutton, underwear, until, undo, untie, under, unzip, unfold, unhappy, untidy, unclean.

3. uninvited, unbutton, undo, untie, unzip, unfold, unhappy, untidy, unclean

4. unbalanced, unfair, unable, uncomfortable, unsteady, unload

5. (a) untrue   (b) unwell   (c) unclear   (d) unequal
   (e) unfair   (f) unfriendly   (g) unlock   (h) unpleasant
   (i) unpopular   (j) unwilling

Additional activities

Pupils can:

1. Write short poems using words containing one particular prefix or suffix; e.g. 'im' or 'ful'.

2. Play games in groups to see who can come up with the most words with a particular prefix/suffix.

3. Break difficult words into parts in an attempt to read them.

4. Make charts of prefixes/suffixes that can be displayed in the classroom.

5. Add new words to personal word books.

Homework suggestion

Give the pupils one prefix/suffix and ask them to write as many words with it as they can.

A prefix is a word or syllable joined to the front of a word to change or add to its meaning.

1 Read this poem as a class.

Uninvited

'Now children, stand up straight and
tall,
the Inspector we need to impress,
you should be proud of your uniform,
Mabel, don't lift up your dress!

Tom, don't unbutton your jacket,
don't flash your underwear!
And Lisa, until the Inspector's gone,
do not undo your hair!

Don't untie your laces, Jake!
Get out from under the chair!
Jim, don't unzip your trousers!
Dave, your socks are an odd pair!

Jack, don't unfold your handkerchief,
It looks slimy and rather wet,
and you shouldn't all look so unhappy,
we'll be the best she's ever met!

Lorraine, you still look untidy,
and Joseph, your face is unclean!'
Oh why do we have to look good for this
guest?
It's not the blinking queen!'

2 Underline all the words that start with 'un'.

Sometimes, 'un' can make a word opposite in meaning.

3 Write 6 words from the poem where this is true.

_____ _____

_____ _____

_____ _____

4 Circle each word where 'un' makes it opposite in meaning:

universe	unit
unbalanced	uncomfortable
unfair	unsteady
under	uncle
unable	unload

5 Make these words opposite by adding 'un':

> All this work makes me uneasy!

(a) true _____

(b) well _____

(c) clear _____

(d) equal _____

(e) fair _____

(f) friendly _____

(g) lock _____

(h) pleasant _____

(i) popular _____

(j) willing _____

Correct yourself

Objective

Continue to self-correct reading errors

Activities covered

- Listening to teacher read
- Reading poem to partner
- Taking note of partner's mistakes
- Self-assessing and improving reading
- Pronouncing words
- Discussing with the class

Background information

Read the poem to the class with all the correct pronunciations. The pupils should be encouraged to correct their own mistakes when reading aloud.

Marmoset an ape, can be as small as a rat, about 1 ½ kg, found in Brazil
Baboon largest monkey, lives in troops, long fangs, lives in Africa
Mangabey medium-sized monkey from West Africa, has facial expression, good communication
Capuchin famous for being used by organ players, intelligent, derived from French word for skullcap
Macaque found in Asia, used in AIDS research
Chimpanzee best tool users after humans
Tamarin like a small lion, from Brazil
Orangutan means 'man of the forest', lives in Borneo and Sumatra
Spider monkey hardly leaves the trees at all, has no thumbs, from South America
Vervet monkey found in Africa, makes different sounds for predators
Gorilla largest ape
Howler monkey from South America, voice travels 5 km in the rainforest
Chacma baboon Southern part of Africa, large teeth
Gibbon South-East Asia, smallest and most agile of the apes
Bonobo Pygmy chimp, found in forests along the Congo River
Lemur carried in their mother's mouths until they can hang on to her, found in Madagascar
Potto has horny spines along its backbone for defence, found in Africa
Tarsier size of a squirrel, found in South-East Asia
Samango monkey rare, very intelligent, found in South Africa

Before the lesson

Check the pronunciation of the different words on the copymaster.

Prepare pictures of the different types of monkeys so the pupils can visualise these creatures as they are reading. (See 'Websites' for suitable pictures).

Divide the class into pairs.

The lesson

1. Read the poem to the class. Explain to the pupils that they will be reading to each other and they must try to correct themselves when they make a mistake.
2. Share prepared pictures of the different species of monkeys.
3. In pairs, the pupils read the poem to each other. They then swap poems and mark on the other's worksheet where errors occurred when reading.
4. The pupils read the poem to each other again, observing any marks their partner has made on their poem.
5. The pupils assess their reading by completing Questions 4(a) and (b).
6. Still in pairs, the pupils attempt reading the given list of animals.
7. All these words are then discussed as a class, and the pupils tick the words they pronounced correctly.

Answers

1. – 7. Teacher check

Additional activities

Pupils can:

1. Self-correct reading errors which occur while reading a class reader aloud.
2. Set up a buddy-reading scheme where the pupils listen to each other reading. They are at all times encouraged to correct themselves when they make a mistake.
3. Read passages that are full of mistakes. This is to give practice in reading and understanding what they read, so that they know when something does not make sense.

Homework suggestion

The pupils read the same poem to a family member.

Recommended reading

Where's that gorilla? by John Coldwell

or a book of poems by Christian Stevens entitled
Animal alphabet

Websites

<www.monkeyzone.com>
<www.kidsturncentral.com/links/monkeylinks.htm>

If you make a mistake when you are reading, do not worry!
The important thing is to correct yourself and carry on.

1 Listen to the teacher read this poem:

2 Read the poem to a partner.

3 Swap poems and underline where your partner is going wrong. (Make sure your partner corrects his/her own mistakes.)

4 Read the poem to each other again, being careful! where it is underlined.

(a) How many mistakes did you make this time?

(b) How many mistakes did you correct yourself?

5 Read the poem together.

6 Still in your pairs, try pronouncing these animal names.

(a) orangutan .... □

(b) spider monkey .... □

(c) vervet monkey .... □

(d) gorilla .... □

(e) howler monkey .... □

(f) chacma baboon .... □

(g) gibbon .... □

(h) bonobo .... □

(i) lemur .... □

(j) potto .... □

(k) tarsier .... □

(l) samango monkey .... □

Thank goodness!

I **am** glad I am not a monkey,
  A marmoset or a baboon,
I'd have to eat insects for breakfast,
  And dine on bananas at noon!

I **am** glad I am not a monkey,
  A mangabey or capuchin,
I'd have to hang onto my mother,
  And scrounge for snacks in the bin!

I **am** glad I am not a monkey,
  A macaque or a chimpanzee,
I'd have to hang upside down by my tail,
  And spend my life in a tree!

I **am** glad I am not a monkey,
  Or a tamarin all in a flap,
I'd have to nibble my sister's fleas,
  I am glad that I am a chap!

> A male orangutan makes burping noises to scare off other males!

7 Discuss the difficult words with your teacher and the class. Tick them if you got the pronunciation right.

Objective

Become an increasingly independent reader

Activities covered

- Reading a poem on his/her own
- Underlining difficult words
- Reading as a class
- Assessing reading
- Making up dishes and reading them
- Discussing a 'saying'

Background information

Pupils need to be given opportunities to read on their own. The pupils can read parts of the class reader, other poems, newspaper articles, information for a project, each other's work etc. It is not only important that pupils read different material but they must understand what they are reading. Comprehension is dependent on the material being suitable for the reader. Pupils must be taught different strategies for reading.

Before the lesson

Select a text for the pupils to read on their own, either at the end of the lesson, or for homework.

The lesson

1. The pupils read the poem on their own. They must try to work out harder words for themselves, so the teacher or fellow pupils should not help.
2. The pupils underline the words they found difficult to read.
3. The class reads the poem together. Explain harder words, such as: 'variety' (selection), 'stroganoff' (Russian dish made from beef, mushrooms and cream), pâté (paste made from meat or fish), 'stir-fry' (cooking food quickly over high heat, originating in China), 'course' (part of a meal), 'sauerkraut' (pickled cabbage, German).
4. The pupils assess whether they had the given list of words correct or incorrect to answer Question 4.
5. The pupils practise saying the words for a few minutes.
6. The pupils make up some worm dishes. They can then read these to the class.
7. Discuss the saying: ***'can of worms'*** as a class to complete Question 6.

Answers

1. – 6. Teacher check

Additional activities

Pupils can:

1. Read their own work to the class.
2. Read books that interest them and participate in silent reading periods in the classroom. Visits to the school and/or local library should be frequent.
3. Undertake reading and comprehension exercises on their own.
4. Research for projects in other subjects.

Homework suggestion

Give the pupils a piece of text to read, testing them the following day.

1 Read this poem to yourself.

If there are words you don't know, try to work them out!

Worm weary

'I'm sick and tired of eating worms!'
said baby bird to Mum,
'The world is full of tasty treats,
and I am needing some!

It's worms on toast for breakfast,
worms for afternoon tea,
worms on my school sandwiches,
I want some variety!

Worm stroganoff and worm pâté,
Worm stir-fry and worm sauce,
Worm muffins and worm custard,
It's worms for every course!

Some that look like spaghetti,
And some like sauerkraut,
I don't want to see another one!
I'm simply all wormed out!'

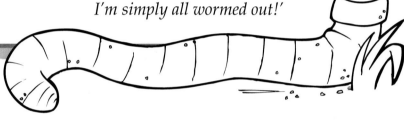

The largest earthworm is found in South Africa and can grow up to 6.5 m long!

2 Underline the words you found difficult.

3 Read the poem as a class.

4 Did you get these words correct?

Tick them if you did.

(a) treats .... ☐

(b) stir-fry .... ☐

(c) variety .... ☐

(d) custard .... ☐

(e) stroganoff .... ☐

(f) spaghetti .... ☐

(g) pâté .... ☐

(h) sauerkraut .... ☐

Make sure you can read them all now!

5 Make up some other worm dishes. Yum!

worm _____

worm _____

worm _____

worm _____

worm _____

Read them aloud!

6 Discuss the saying **'can of worms'** as a class.

Certain worms are a good source of protein!

Objective

Understand the relationship between text and illustration

Activities covered

- Colouring in pictures to go with a poem
- Drawing a character from a poem
- Writing a sentence to go with a character
- Viewing and evaluating illustrated books

Background information

Illustrations will often give more information or make the information in a text more accessible. Pupils are drawn to illustrations as they satisfy part of their curiosity. In this lesson, the pupils learn that the illustration relates to the text. Illustrations add interest, and, for pupils, a page with text and illustrations is less daunting than a whole page of text. (For adults too!) A picture is a quick and easy way to get a message across; e.g. describing spaghetti bolognese is tricky, but a picture will quickly explain it. The copymaster will not take long to complete. There should be plenty of time for the pupils to look through books with illustrations. When the pupils are looking through the reading material, they should not just be looking at the pictures but looking to see how the text relates to the pictures. Tell the pupils they must see if the pictures match the words.

Before the lesson

Prepare a selection of books and other reading material that use illustrations and/or photos; e.g. newspapers, nonfiction books, storybooks, magazines, recipe books etc.

Show a picture of a Harley-Davidson® motorcycle (optional).

The lesson

1. Read the poem as a class. The poem can be discussed as well as the title. Words that may need clarification are 'gung-ho', 'leathers', 'Harley-Davidson®' and 'wheelie'.
2. The pupils colour in pictures that go with the poem to complete Question 1.
3. For Question 2, they draw the character in the poem, taking their clues from the poem.
4. The pupils write a sentence to describe the picture of a character.
5. The pupils look at reading material that contains illustrations and/or photos and see how the pictures relate to the text to complete Question 4. Some of these can be shared as a class.

Answers

1. glass of beer / dragon / hot dog and chips
2. – 4. Teacher check

Additional activities

Pupils can:

1. Read a range of texts that contain illustrations; e.g. newspapers, story books, nonfiction books, magazines and comic strips. Look at advertisements and see how the pictures or photos in them relates to each product.
2. Write sentences. Then draw a picture to suit the sentence.
3. Write about a given drawing.
4. Write a story in pictures.
5. Look at instructions that have step-by-step illustrations.

Homework suggestion

The pupils can bring to class something from home that uses text and illustrations/photos. All examples can be displayed in the classroom.

Recommended reading

(Poems to draw accompanying pictures)

The man who invented football by Kit Wright
Sky in the pie by Roger McGough
Things to find in teacher's trouser turn-ups by Paul Cookson
The planet teacher by Andrew Collett
Mother's pride by Damian Harvey
Dressing up by John Coldwell
My knickers by Ann Ziety
Take off that hat by Ted Scheu

Websites

(for illustrated stories)

<www.storyplace.org>
<www.uptoten.com/kids> (animated stories)
<www.wiredforbooks.org/kids.htm>/ (Beatrix Potter)

When we are reading, pictures can help!

1 Colour in the pictures you think suit this poem.

Gung-ho Gran

My grandma is a biker,
She's really tough and mean.
She's always dressed in leathers,
From when she was a teen.

Her long, grey hair is knotty,
With just one streak of red.
She has a tattoo on her arm,
Of a dragon's head.

She has big boots with buckles,
That jangle when she walks,
Her neck chains clang together,
Like her tongue stud when she talks.

She rides a Harley-Davidson®,
And of it she is proud.
She can even pull a wheelie,
Just to impress the crowd.

She cannot bake or cook a thing,
But loves hot dogs and chips,
And pints of ice-cold beer,
Disappear between her lips.

But when I'm feeling lonely,
I know that she'll be true,
And cuddle me warmly in her lap,
Like other grandmas do.

2 Draw Gung-ho Gran.

3 Write a sentence to describe this character.

_____

_____

_____

_____

4 Look at books with illustrations.

Name one. _____

Did the illustrations suit the words? ☐ Yes ☐ No

Explain. _____

Objective

Refine his/her listening skills through hearing the teacher read aloud

Activities covered

- Listening to the teacher
- Answering questions
- Discussing a poem and answers to questions about the poem
- Drawing vegetables

Background information

Pupils must be told to listen carefully when the teacher is reading, as they will be answering questions about what they have heard. Teachers should often be asking questions after pupils have listened to something. Testing their listening skills on a regular basis will keep pupils 'on their toes' and get them used to listening carefully to detail.

Before the lesson

Have the poem ready to read to the class (see below).

Prepare pictures of various types of vegetables. (Many pupils do not know their vegetables!)

The lesson

1. Hold a general class discussion about different types of vegetables. Show the pupils the prepared pictures. The importance of vegetables in our diet could also be mentioned.
2. Read the poem *'Veggie veto'* to the class.
3. The pupils complete Questions 2 – 5. This must be done on their own without any discussion.
4. The pupils can then complete Questions 6 and 7.
5. The teacher can read the poem again, then discuss the answers with the pupils.

Answers

1. Teacher check
2. carrots, potatoes, spinach, mushrooms, beans, cabbage
3. (a) in a white, creamy sauce
   (b) boiled
   (c) lightly fried
4. (a) yellow
   (b) green
5. (a) tomatoes
   (b) potatoes
   (c) spinach
   (d) carrots
6. We don't know, because he has never tried them before.
7. Teacher check

Additional activities

Pupils can:

1. Read texts from other learning areas such as geography, and then have a 'spot quiz' to see how well the pupils listened.
2. Listen to poems or short stories and then answer questions about the details in the poem/story. (Roald Dahl's *Revolting rhymes* are good for this exercise.)

Poem for the teacher to read:

Veggie veto

Delicious baby cabbage,
small and sweet and round,
crunchy, orange carrots,
pulled fresh from the ground.

Cauliflower cheese,
with its white and creamy sauce,
potatoes, soft and mushy,
are always on the course.

Forest-green courgette,
and an aubergine lightly fried,
a large and boiled turnip,
with pumpkin on the side.

Tomatoes plump and juicy,
spinach, finely chopped,
tasty yellow sweetcorn,
green beans tailed and topped.

Broccoli, peas and mushrooms,
mangetout, I dare say!
parsnips, leeks and peppers,
I'll try them out one day.

Recommended reading

(For listening)

Glunk by Leo Aylen
Food for thought by Michaela Morgan
No peas for the wicked by Roger McGough

I bet you love eating all your vegetables!

1 Listen carefully to the poem.

> What is your favourite vegetable?
>
> What is your least favourite vegetable?

2 Tick which vegetables are mentioned.

cucumber............☐	brussel sprouts.....☐	sweet potatoes.....☐
carrots ....☐	spinach................☐	celery..................☐
potatoes ....☐	mushrooms ....☐	chillies.................☐
onions.................☐	beans...................☐	cabbage...............☐

3 According to the poem, how are the following cooked?

(a) cauliflower cheese _____

(b) turnip _____

(c) aubergine _____

4 What colour are these?

(a) sweetcorn _____ (b) courgette _____

5 Which vegetables were described like this?

(a) plump and juicy _____

(b) soft and mushy _____

(c) finely chopped _____

(d) crunchy and orange _____

6 Does the poet like the vegetables listed in the poem? Yes/No/Don't know

Explain. _____

_____

> What did the carrot say to the wheat?
>
> 'Lettuce rest, I'm feeling beet.'

7 Draw these vegetables and colour them.

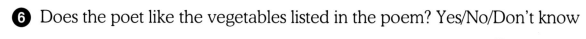

mangetout	pumpkin	cauliflower	parsnip

Objective

Write a poem in the form of a label

Activities covered

- Writing a zoo label
- Checking work
- Rewriting and displaying work
- Having a class vote

Background information

In this lesson, it is important that pupils feel encouraged to write. Even less-able pupils should feel confident to attempt the activity, but the teacher's support is vital. The pupils need to feel some level of success in order to gain confidence with their writing. This encouragement should come from the teacher, as well as other pupils in the class. All good efforts from pupils should be praised.

Before the lesson

The pupils will need the means to rewrite their zoo labels neatly and to display them.

The lesson

1. Hold a class discussion about different zoos. The pupils can briefly tell about an experience they have had at a zoo.
2. Read the unfinished zoo label on the copymaster.
3. The pupils write a zoo 'label'. They can use a real animal or make one up. Encourage pupils to rhyme the words at the ends of the lines if possible.
4. Walk around the class and observe the pupils' work, offering suggestions and helping to correct mistakes.
5. The pupils check their own zoo labels, then rewrite them neatly or type them and display them.
6. The class can vote anonymously for the best creature. Additional 'awards' for different categories, such as 'most unusual' or 'excellent detail' etc. could be given to selected pupils.

Answers

1. – 3. Teacher check

Additional activities

Pupils can:

1. Participate in regular writing competitions in the class, focusing on different aspects so that they all get the chance to win a prize.
2. Begin a 'Writer's gallery' where work is displayed each week.
3. Write and post letters.
4. Create class anthologies of the class's poetry.
5. Keep portfolios of their work to look through.
6. Display their written work in the classroom, school and in the local community.
7. Send their work to newspapers or magazines.
8. Write for visitors coming to the school or write about special occasions happening within the school. These could be included on the school's website or newspaper.

Homework suggestion

The pupils read their zoo 'labels' to a family member.

Have you ever been to a zoo? Most of the cages have labels on them to describe the animals.

1 You are going to write a label.
It can be for a real animal or a made-up one.

Name of creature: _____

Lives in _____

Comes out _____

Often _____

_____

The colour of _____

The size of _____

Eats _____

Notice how it _____

_____

Making a strange sound, like _____

Beware _____

Do not _____ Ever.

Picture:

2 Check your work. Rewrite it and display it.

3 Have a class vote for the best creature. What is it? _____

I can't write a poem!

Objective

Observe the teacher modelling different writing genres

Activities covered

- Reading a poem
- Observing the teacher write a poem
- Writing an excuse poem
- Reading own poetry to self

Background information

Often, pupils will groan when told they will be writing a poem. This lesson proves just how easy it is to write one. Rhyming is not necessary. The idea of the lesson is for the pupils to watch the teacher create an example of the given poem, getting ideas from the pupils themselves. The teacher should write the poem on the board and leave it there for the duration of the lesson.

Before the lesson

Practise writing a poem in preparation for the lesson (see Question 2). Think of possible ideas to guide the pupils.

The lesson

1. Read the poem as a class.
2. Model a poem on the board, getting ideas from the pupils. The poem should take the structure of a list of excuses and need not rhyme. This example can be left on the board.
3. The pupils write a poem by listing the excuses as to why they cannot write a poem. Encourage them to use their own ideas as much as possible. They should write full sentences.
4. The pupils read the poem to themselves and assess their efforts by completing Question 4.
5. The finished poems can be read out in class or displayed.

Answers

1. – 4. Teacher check

Additional activities

Pupils can:

1. See, by teacher example, various writing techniques such as poetry, short stories, paragraphs, letters etc.
2. Make a booklet of their poems called 'Why our class can't write poems'. This can be left in the school library so that others can read it.

Recommended reading

(excuses)

The wolf's excuse by Yvonne Coppard

No time by Alison Chisholm

Excuse my excuse by Brian Patten

The worst excuses in the world by Clare Bevan

The excuse by Jane Wright

Do you think writing a poem is hard?

❶ Read this poem.

I can't write a poem!

There are many reasons, teacher,
Why I can't write this poem,
My thumb is sore for one thing,
And I think I should go home.

There's not enough space on my page,
My pen is running dry,
My chair is quite uncomfortable,
Besides, I'm not a poetic guy!

I have a bit of a headache,
And there is too much noise,
The air in here is very stale,
And poems are not for boys!

So, teacher, please forgive me,
I cannot do this task,
When you ask me to be a poet,
I won't! So please don't ask!

❷ Now watch your teacher write a similar poem. Give the teacher some of your ideas.

❸ It's your turn to write a poem about not being able to write a poem! Use as many excuses as you can. Your poem does not have to rhyme.

You can't use these excuses for real!

I can't write a poem!

List your excuses here.

_____

_____

_____

_____

_____

_____

_____

_____

You just wrote a poem!

❹ Read your poem to yourself. Colour a face to show what you thought of it.

Read and write

Objective

Use personal reading as a stimulus to writing

Activities covered

- Reading an example of a poetry form
- Writing a cinquain about a character
- Rating a poem
- Drawing a scene

Background information

For this lesson, the pupils can read a book, article, story, poem etc. as long as there is enough information for them to write the poem. The poem is called a cinquain. The pupils should not be too concerned about the syllables, as long as it is close to the numbers given. The poem should focus on a character in the book or story they have read.

Before the lesson

The pupils will need to have read a complete text—e.g. a story—containing at least one character.

The lesson

1. The pupils write the name of the character.
2. Read the example of the cinquain on the copymaster with the class.
3. The pupils then write their own cinquain about a character from their chosen text. They should try to use the same number of words in each line if possible, but should not be so concerned about the amount of syllables.
4. The pupils read their poems and give them a rating to complete Question 4.
5. The pupils draw a scene from their chosen text.

Answers

1. – 5. Teacher check

Additional activities

Pupils can:

1. Undertake writing activities about other texts they have read, such as recipes, advertisements, brochures etc.
2. Display their cinquains in the classroom under the heading 'What we have read.'
3. Write other poems based on books they have read.
4. Read a story/short story and continue the story after the ending.
5. Read articles and write their viewpoint.
6. Write reviews for material they have read; e.g. poems, stories, projects, magazines, comics, lyrics etc.
7. Write a character sketch based on someone they read about.
8. Write a comic strip based on something they have read.

A cinquain is a type of five-line poem.

Write a cinquain about a character in a book or story you have read.

1 What character did you choose? _____

2 Follow this example:

> *2 syllables, 1 word, title* .... Wormwood,
>
> *4 syllables, 2 words, describing title* ....clever, unloved,
>
> *6 syllables, 3 words, expressing action*...........................reading, wishing, plotting,
>
> *8 syllables, 4 words, expressing feeling* .... Lucky having super powers,
>
> *2 syllables, another word for title* ....Mathilda.

3 Do your own!

> *2 syllables, 1 word, title*   _____
>
> *4 syllables, 2 words, describing title*   _____
>
> *6 syllables, 3 words, expressing action* _____
>
> *8 syllables, 4 words, expressing feeling* _____
>
> *2 syllables, another word for title*   _____

4 Rate your poem (3 books is the best!).

5 Draw a scene from the book or story you chose, involving your character.

Story poem

Objective

Write a story-poem

Activities covered

- Writing a story-poem
- Reading a poem to self and improving it
- Drawing pictures to depict a story

Background information

In this lesson, the pupils will be writing a story in poem form. The basic structure is given and pupils will complete the given sentences. Of course, parts of the basic structure could be changed if it is found necessary. In this lesson, rhythm is important. The pupils should use rhyming words if they can. The teacher can suggest a rhyming scheme.

Before the lesson

Read the poem to the pupils.

The lesson

1. Read the example poem. Mention the rhyme and rhythm. Read the poem a second time, slowly, while the pupils clap or beat the rhythm.

2. Read through the unfinished poem on the worksheet so the pupils know what to expect.

3. Allow the pupils time to think about their story.

4. The pupils complete their story-poem trying to maintain a constant rhythm in their poem. They should also use rhyming words where they can.

5. The pupils read their story-poem to themselves, and improve the words or rhythm if they can. They should be told to clap or beat their poem out to make sure that it has rhythm and flows.

6. The pupils draw their story in cartoon form to complete Question 3.

7. After the poems have been finished, they could be shared with the class and displayed in the classroom.

Bear encounter

One day I went out walking,
and met a big, brown bear.
He greeted me with quite a smile,
but all I did was stare.

Of course, I was very frightened,
but he said, 'Please don't fear,
what I'm needing is your help,
my house is very near'.

He beckoned for me to follow,
my steps were shaky and slow.
Could this be a nasty trick?
I'd really love to know.

We came upon a clearing,
with a cottage, neat and quaint.
Was this where they would dine on me?
The thought made me feel faint.

I was led into the kitchen,
where stood Mum and baby bear,
but all they wanted, was for me,
to fix a broken chair!

Answers

1. – 3. Teacher check

Additional activities

Pupils can:

1. Write other types of poems that have a story line, a short story, a fairytale, a short play, a dialogue etc.

2. Change elements of a well-known fairytale; e.g. some of the characters, the ending.

3. Write a story in the form of a comic strip, a flow chart, an episode of a TV programme (preferably with a 'cliff hanger') or a conversation.

4. Create a story picture book for toddlers.

Recommended reading

(poems that tell a story)

Christmas pudding by Charles Thomson
Chicken poxed by Valerie Bloom
Bill's eraser by Terry Jones
The day the animals talked by Terry Jones

1 Try to make an interesting story-poem by completing the sentences below.

One day I went out _____,

And saw a _____,

He _____,

_____.

Of course, I was very _____,

He said, ' _____,

_____,

_____,

He _____,

My _____,

Could this be _____,

_____?

We _____,

With _____,

Was this where _____,

The _____.

I was _____,

_____,

He _____,

_____.

> You can use rhyming words if you want to.

2 Read your poem to yourself. Improve it if you can.

3 Draw pictures to show your story as a cartoon strip.

> Make sure your poem has rhythm! Beat it out!

Enjoy your writing

Objective

Sing and write new versions of a simple song

Activities covered

- Writing a verse of a well-known song
- Singing a song
- Singing different versions of songs
- Writing own song
- Reading, singing and assessing a song
- Assessing songs written by others

Background information

Pupils should not always just be preparing written work for the teacher. They should also have opportunities to read and enjoy what they have written. Taking pleasure in reading their own work should motivate them to be more successful. The pupils should be writing about something that is meaningful to them, or something they find interesting or funny.

Yankee Doodle

Yankee Doodle went to town,
Riding on a pony,
He stuck a feather in his hat,
And called it macaroni.

Before the lesson

Have the pupils read texts they have written.

Revise the words of the first verse of *'Yankee Doodle'*. (See the Background information section.)

The lesson

1. The pupils write the words to the first verse of the song *'Yankee Doodle'*.
2. Sing the words as a class, then try the two versions given.
3. The pupils write their own version of the song to complete Question 4, attempting to make lines 2 and 4 rhyme. The correct stresses are quite difficult but need not be perfect.
4. The pupils sing their versions to themselves and assess them by colouring music notes for Question 5.
5. The pupils share their songs with the class. (They do not have to sing them if they do not wish to!)
6. The pupils vote for the best version of the song and write it to complete Question 7.

Answers

1. – 7. Teacher check

Additional activities

Pupils can:

1. Read other written work they have done, such as stories, poems and letters etc.
2. Write about something good that has happened to them, and re-read it.
3. Write a list poem about things that annoy them.
4. Write a letter to a family member/friend far away and post it.
5. Write about their intentions for the summer and re-read it.
6. Keep a portfolio of their best work and read through it from time to time.

Homework suggestion

The pupils read/sing their song again to themselves, and then read/sing it to a family member or pet.

Remember the song 'Yankee Doodle'?

1 Write the first verse below.

_____

_____

_____

_____

2 Sing it together as a class.   **3** Sing these versions. (Use the same tune!)

> *Yankee Doodle went to town,*
> *Riding on a tow truck,*
> *He travelled on the country roads,*
> *And in the mud he got stuck.*

> *Yankee Doodle went to Spain,*
> *Riding on a pony,*
> *He wanted to eat chorizo,*
> *But only found baloney.*

Sing your heart out!

4 Try one yourself! Try to make lines 2 and 4 rhyme.

Yankee Doodle _____

_____

_____

_____

Sing it to yourself quietly!

5 How well did your song turn out?
Colour in a score out of 5.

6 Share your song with the class. (You don't have to sing it!)

7 Have a class vote for the best version. Write it below: (If it is yours, draw a big star instead!)

_____

_____

_____

_____

Picnic time

Objective

Choose the audience for which to write

Activities covered

- Choosing an age group
- Discussing intended audiences
- Writing a picnic poem in draft form
- Checking poem
- Rewriting and decorating
- Discussing completed poems

Background information

The teacher will need to provide examples of how specific audiences are targeted; e.g. books, advertisements, magazines, food labels. The teacher can bring a few examples to class and ask the pupils who they think the advert/book/comic etc. is aimed at. Pupils can comment on how the specific audience has been targeted; e.g. wording, music, colour. The teacher can write a list on the board of aspects the pupils must consider when writing their poem, such as type of writing, size of writing, message, vocabulary used, picture, colour, style, grammar, language, detail etc. For this lesson, the audience is targeted, not only in the use of vocabulary and content, but also in the presentation, which must also suit the audience.

Before the lesson

The teacher should have several examples of books, adverts, magazines, food labels etc. to show pupils how different audiences are targeted.

Pupils should be familiar with alliteration.

The lesson

1. The teacher discusses the examples he/she has brought to the class.
2. Pupils choose the age group they are going to write for.
3. The class holds a discussion about how different audiences can be targeted when writing their picnic poem. A few letters can be chosen and completed as a group using alliteration where possible.
4. Pupils write their picnic poem on the copymaster in draft form, keeping their audiences in mind. The teacher can tell the pupils that alliteration will make the poem more effective.
5. Pupils reread their poem, checking it carefully and making sure it suits the audience for whom they are writing.
6. Pupils rewrite their poem neatly and decorate it. Remind them that the presentation must also be appropriate for their audience.
7. The poems are displayed in an appropriate section of the school.
8. All poems can be discussed as a class.

Answers

1. – 4. Teacher check

Example for Question 2

angry apples

butter biscuits

crunchy crisps etc.

Additional activities

Pupils can:

1. Choose their audience when writing: stories, letters, adverts, product labels etc.
2. Write thank-you letters to grandparents.
3. Write a letter of complaint to a family member/actor/character in a book.
4. Write a letter to a friend using slang words.
5. Write text messages to a friend, parent, uncle etc.

Website

< www.ability.org.uk/kids_recipes.html>

Write a picnic poem.

1 First, decide who your poem will be written for. Tick the box.

5 – 7-year-olds.....................☐

8 – 11-year-olds.................☐

12 years – teenagers ....☐

adults ....☐

2 Write a picnic poem. Use alliteration; e.g. angry apples, butter biscuits.

In the picnic basket, we will pack:

a _____	n _____
b _____	o _____
c _____	p _____
d _____	q _____
e _____	r _____
f _____	s _____
g _____	t _____
h _____	u _____
i _____	v _____
j _____	w _____
k _____	x _____
l _____	y _____
m _____	z _____

3 Read your poem and check it.

4 Rewrite your poem on a separate sheet and decorate it to match the age group for whom it was written. Display the poems where your audience can read them.

> Alliteration will make your poem more effective! Remember who you are writing the poem for and make it suitable for this age group!

Objective

Receive and give positive responses to writing

Activities covered

- Reading poems
- Commenting on poems and giving scores
- Writing own poem
- Reading own poem to group
- Commenting on others' poems
- Giving scores to poems
- Improving own poem

Background information

In this lesson, the pupils must comment positively on others' work. Tell them that they should be kind to each other, and make suggestions if they think a poem could be improved.

Before the lesson

Divide the class into groups.

Other examples of *'Roses are red'* poems may be provided (see URL).

The lesson

1. Read the *'Roses are red'* poems with the class.
2. Explain that you want positive feedback on the poems. In groups, the pupils make suggestions on how the poems can be improved, but should do so in a kindly manner. They can then score each of the poems out of 10.
3. The pupils write a 'Roses are red' poem of their own. They may swap the order of the first two lines or change some of the words; e.g., such as 'Violets are blue, Roses are red' or 'Roses are red, Daisies are white . . .' etc.
4. The pupils read their poem to their group. The group should make positive comments and give constructive criticism only. The group then scores the poem. The pupils write two of the comments they received to complete Question 5.
5. The pupils improve their poem if necessary, following helpful suggestions from the group, to complete Question 6.

Answers

1. – 6. Teacher check

Additional activities

Pupils can:

1. Comment on each other's work, in groups, giving an award for the best work.
2. In groups, or as a class, work together on a poem, project, story etc. – giving each other advice and positive feedback.

Homework suggestion

Have the pupils write another 'Roses are red' poem and read it to their family.

Website

(roses are red)

<www.gigglepoetry.com/poetryclass/roses.html>

When reading the work of others, you should try to be positive. You should give suggestions if you think they could improve it, but do so nicely!

1 Read these in a group.

(a)

Roses are red,
Violets are blue,
My friends love burgers,
But I prefer stew.

/10

(c)

Roses are red,
Violets are blue,
What we get up to,
Mum hasn't a clue.

/10

(b)

Rose is a little red,
Violet's turning blue,
The pair of them do not look well,
I think they have the flu.

/10

(d)

Violets are blue,
Roses are red,
School is OK,
But I prefer bed.

/10

2 Discuss the poems. Put a score out of 10 next to each.

3 Write a poem of your own.

> Keep the rhyme scheme the same!
> (i.e. the second and fourth lines should rhyme.)

_____

_____

_____

_____

4 Read your poem to your group. Ask them to comment on it.

> Be honest but kind!

5 (a) Write down two words the group used when assessing your poem.

_____   _____

(b) What score did they give you out of 5?   /5

(c) Did you think the group's assessment was fair? Write why or why not.

_____

_____

_____

6 Improve your poem if you can. Follow any helpful suggestions you received.

Bending the truth

Objective

Write a poem that uses exaggeration

Activities covered

- Giving exaggerations orally
- Writing an example of an exaggeration
- Identifying possible exaggerations
- Reading a poem
- Underlining exaggerations
- Writing an exaggeration poem
- Reading own poem to self
- Reading own poem to class

Background information

Pupils should have their writing valued by reading it aloud to others, displaying it in the classroom or school, having visitors read their work, making class anthologies of their work, submitting their work to poetry competitions, having class awards, holding a poetry competition etc. This lesson is about exaggerating and it should be explained to the pupils that exaggerating is not a good idea because it is just the same as lying!

Before the lesson

Other examples of exaggerations could be provided.

The lesson

1. Discuss what an exaggeration is. The pupils give exaggerations as a class, orally, about school. They can then complete Question 1.

2. The pupils tick which sentences are possible exaggerations to complete Question 2. This could be done as a class.

3. Read the poem *'My wonderful cat'*. Discuss harder words or phrases such as 'outdoes', 'cryptic clues' and 'soufflé'.

4. The pupils underline possible exaggerations in the poem to complete Question 4. Discuss this as a class.

5. The pupils write their own poem by listing exaggerations about their family. These should be full sentences, with each new sentence starting on a new line. Rhyming is not essential. Encourage the pupils to draft their poems on scrap paper first.

6. The pupils read their poems to themselves and then to the class.

Answers

1. Teacher check
2. possible exaggerations: (a), (d), (e)
3. – 6. Teacher check

Additional activities

Pupils can:

1. Collect all the poems and collate them in booklet form, titled 'Do not exaggerate!' Leave it in the school library for others to read.

2. Hold award ceremonies in the classroom on a frequent basis.

3. Display their work in the classroom/in the school/in the school newspaper/on the school website/for visitors.

4. Hold class writing competitions.

5. Write a class newspaper.

6. Put together booklets of the same written task written by different pupils and give these 'books' a title. Display them where others can read them.

7. Keep a portfolio of all their best written work.

Homework suggestion

The pupils read their exaggeration poem to a family member.

Recommended reading

I'm much better than you
by Colin McNaughton

To exaggerate means to make something seem better or worse or more amazing than it really is.

> I've told you a thousand times not to exaggerate!

1 As a class, think of some exaggerations about school.

Write one. _____

2 Tick the sentences below you think are exaggerations.

(a) **I can read one hundred pages in one minute!** ... ☐

(b) **My bike is so big even my dad can ride it!** .... ☐

(c) **My kitten is so small it can fit in my hand!** .... ☐

(d) **My grandmother is two hundred years old!** .... ☐

(e) **My brother is taller than a giraffe!** .... ☐

3 Read the poem.

4 Underline the exaggerations in the poem.

5 Write a poem about your family, using exaggerations. Use full sentences. Plan your poem on a separate sheet of paper first.

Of course you know you should never exaggerate!

My wonderful cat

I have the cleverest cat in the world,
She outdoes others by far,
She sings in the local choir,
And can play the bass guitar.

She helps me with my homework,
Does fractions with such ease,
She knows her ancient history,
And can name the different trees.

She reads the daily papers,
She knows all the latest news,
She even does the crosswords,
That have the cryptic clues.

She's been known to cook the dinner,
And can make a cheese soufflé,
She sets the table beautifully,
Or serves it on a tray.

Yes, my cat is quite special,
I think you should come and see,
There's really nothing she can't do,
She's almost as special as me!

6 Read your poem to yourself and then to the class.

As lovely as school

Objective

Use similes

Activities covered

- Discussing similes
- Writing similes
- Completing similes
- Writing a simile poem
- Assessing a simile poem

Background information

This lesson should contain much oral discussion. Encourage the pupils to orally use the similes in full sentences. Similes should be displayed in the classroom and pupils should use them in their writing.

Before the lesson

Prepare a list of other well-known similes.

The lesson

1. The class discusses similes and the pupils write three examples.
2. Read the poem *'As good as ...'* as a class.
3. Pupils complete Question 3.
4. The pupils write their own simile poem. Explain to the pupils that in order to make the poem original, they should make up their own similes by thinking of something that is 'strong', 'cute', 'smart' etc. They can change 'a' to 'an' if they need to.
5. The pupils read their simile poem to themselves and comment on it, using one or more similes.
6. The poems can be displayed, written neatly, typed out, or read to the class.

Answers

1. – 2. Teacher check
3.   (a) peacock   (b) fox   (c) house
         (d) snail/tortoise   (e) bat   (f) ox
4. – 5. Teacher check

Additional activities

Pupils can:

1. Repeat the lesson using local words and sayings, common English phrases, idioms, proverbs, common expressions etc.
2. Discuss slang words and have a 'no slang' day.
3. Look at the origin of a few words, especially those borrowed from other languages, such as 'spaghetti', 'khaki' or 'chocolate'.
4. Discuss local community sayings, sayings that are used only in their own country and some from other countries.
5. Discuss local community expressions and their possible origins.
6. Look at place names nearby and find possible origins of the names.
7. Look at traditional songs of their own country and study the language used.

Homework suggestion

The pupils ask a family member to help them write more similes. These can be discussed the following day at school.

Websites

(Irish sayings)

<www.irish-sayings.com>

(English sayings)

<www.rootsweb.com/~genepool/sayings.htm>

(American sayings)

<http://prospects.leeuniversity.edu/info/international/
pre-arrival/sayings.asp>

Recommended reading

Today I feel ... by Gervase Phinn
The reader of this poem by Roger McGough

Similes compare one thing with another using 'like' or 'as'; e.g. as cute as a button.

Kids are as good as gold!

1 Discuss similes as a class. Write down three.

_____

_____

_____

2 Read this poem. The poet has made up his/her own similes!

3 Complete these well-known similes.

(a) As proud as a _____

(b) As cunning as a _____

(c) As large as a _____

(d) As slow as a _____

(e) As blind as a _____

(f) As strong as an _____

4 Make up your own simile poem with new similes.

5 Read your poem to yourself. Use similes to write what you think of your poem. Be positive if you can!

My poem is as good as

_____

_____

_____

_____

As good as ...

I'm as sleepy as a cat,
And as slimy as a snail,
As proud as a gorilla,
And as graceful as a whale.

I'm as hungry as a piglet,
And as silly as a clown,
As strong as King Kong,
And as busy as my town.

I'm as fit as a rock star,
And as wholesome as stew,
As grotesque as a teacher,
But not as ugly as you!

As sweet as a teacher!

I am ...

As sweet as a _____,

As strong as a _____,

As cute as a _____,

As smart as a _____,

As super as a _____,

As kind as a _____,

As fit as a _____,

As lovely as a _____,

As busy as a _____,

As neat as a _____,

As proud as a _____,

As perfect as a _____.

No thanks!

Objective

Become aware of new words and new connotations of words through his/her reading and writing experience

Activities covered

- Reading a poem
- Working out possible meanings of words as a group
- Writing sentences to illustrate word meanings
- Summing up each verse of a poem
- Discussing as a class

Background information

When pupils learn new words, it is important that they practise using the words, both orally and in written form. Ask pupils to give sentences using the new words so that they can be used in context. New words can be written in a word book and/or displayed in the classroom, where the pupils can refer to them when they are writing.

Before the lesson

Divide the class into groups.

The lesson

1. Read the poem *'Thanks, but no thanks'* as a class.
2. The pupils read the poem in their groups.
3. As a group, the pupils try to determine the meanings of the words in the list. They can underline these words in the poem and then write a full sentence showing they understand the meaning of the word to complete Question 2. Dictionaries can be used.
4. The pupils sum up each verse of the poem by writing a sentence.
5. The poem and all questions are then discussed as a class.
6. If there is time, the pupils can give oral sentences using the new vocabulary.

Answers

1. Teacher check
2. Answers will vary but should indicate the following meanings:
   (a) precious – very valuable
   (b) generous – willing to give things or share them
   (c) daily – every day
   (d) appreciate – enjoy or value something
   (e) deceased – dead
   (f) rodent – animal that has large front teeth for gnawing
   (g) efforts – energy used to …
3. Possible answers: My pet brings me a dead rodent. I appreciate the gift. He went to a lot of trouble. I would prefer not to get a gift more than once a year.
4. Teacher check

Additional activities

Pupils can:

1. In groups, receive one or two new words from the poem. The pupils draw the meanings, writing the word below the picture. These can then be displayed in the classroom.
2. Write all new words in word books.
3. Discuss new words as a class and use them in oral sentences.
4. Draw word meanings and display these in the classroom.
5. Use new words in conversation and writing.

Homework suggestion

Choose five new words and write five sentences. The pupils can then use the new vocabulary at home.

1 Read this poem as a class.

Thanks, but no thanks

My precious, generous, lovable cat,
Daily brings to me,
A feathery or furry gift,
As dead as dead can be.

Now please don't get me wrong,
I appreciate the thought.
A deceased rodent is a super gift,
Especially one he's caught.

I appreciate his efforts,
In shopping for the best.
I know the skill that is required,
In conquering his quest.

I only ask that he be prudent,
My birthday comes once a year,
He shouldn't be spoiling me so much,
'Thanks, but no thanks, dear'.

At the back of a cat's eye, a special layer reflects light. This means that it can see even in very dim light!

2 Read the poem as a group.

What do you think these words mean? For each word, write a full sentence that shows its meaning.

(a) precious _____

(b) generous _____

(c) daily _____

(d) appreciate _____

(e) deceased _____

(f) rodent _____

(g) efforts _____

3 Sum up each verse in Question 1 by writing one sentence in each box.

4 Discuss all your answers with the class.

Poem hunt

Objective

Select personal reading material and develop personal taste in reading for pleasure and information

Activities covered

- Writing about a favourite poem
- Identifying a favourite part
- Drawing a picture that depicts poem
- Sharing a poem with a group
- Voting for the best poem

Background information

Pupils need to be able to choose their own reading material so they can read something that suits their own personal taste. They should be able to visit the school/local library on a regular basis. Encourage the pupils to choose books that they will enjoy reading, as well as something that suits their reading skill. This lesson could be taken towards the end of the year, after the pupils have been exposed to a wide range of poetry. The school should have several poetry anthologies available for pupils to read.

Before the lesson

The pupils will need to have ready a poem they have read and enjoyed. They should bring a book containing this poem to the lesson if possible or at least details about the book (title, publisher etc.).

Divide the class into groups.

The lesson

1. The pupils complete Questions 1–5. Questions 2, 3 and 4 should be answered with full sentences.
2. The pupils share their poem with a group.
3. All poems are discussed as a group, and the favourite from each group can be read to the class.
4. The class then votes for the best poem.
5. The pupils complete Question 7.

Answers

1. – 7. Teacher check

Additional activities

Pupils can:

1. Write a rhyming couplet about a favourite poem.
2. Hold a class discussion on their favourite types of books or stories.
3. Read something of their choice every week, such as a poem, article, lyrics etc.
4. Look at websites to find out about new books;
   e.g. <www.ukchildrensbooks.com> or <www.thebestkidsbooksite.com>.

For this lesson, you will need a book containing one of your favourite poems.

The famous poet Allan Ahlberg was a postman and gravedigger before he became a teacher!

1 Complete the details.

Title of poem: _____

Poet: _____

Book title: _____

Publisher: _____

2 Read the poem. What makes this poem special?

_____

_____

3 Write one sentence which explains what the poem is about.

_____

_____

4 Describe your favourite part of the poem.

_____

_____

5 Draw a picture that best represents the poem.

[ ]

6 Share your poem with a group.

7 (a) Hold a class vote for the best poem. Write the title and poet below.

_____

(b) Why do you think this poem was so popular?

_____

_____

Let's watch telly

Objective

Experience different types of text

Activities covered

- Reading TV guide in poetry form
- Rewriting guide
- Reading real TV guide
- Writing different programmes

Background information

There are so many different texts the teacher can use in the classroom. Ideas are: concrete poetry, lists, recipes, adverts, plays, song words, websites, newspapers, cartoons, comics, charts etc. This lesson focuses on TV guides.

Before the lesson

Each pupil must have access to a TV guide for one day's viewing. They can each bring one to school.

The lesson

1. Pupils read the TV guide poem on the copymaster.
2. Pupils write the guide in a clearer way using the table. Pupils can make up a name for the TV channel and some of the programmes.
3. Pupils read the TV guide they have brought from home.
4. Pupils write four programmes.
5. The teacher discusses with the class how TV guides are written; e.g. films are often highlighted, information is given for certain programmes, actors and actresses names are sometimes included, programmes and films sometimes have star ratings or reviews and so on.

Answers

1. Teacher check
2. Example:

Channel: Channel Fun		
Time	Programme	Type
3.30 pm	Home and gone	Soap
4.05 pm	The Crump triplets	Cartoon
4.35 pm	Sport today	Football
6.15 pm	Marrow patch	Cartoon
6.40 pm	Pop hero	Music/Talent
7.45 pm	Weather update	Weather
8.00 pm	The Unbelievables	Film

3. Teacher check

Additional activities

Pupils can:

1. Read different texts; e.g. newspapers, magazines, comics, graphs, shopping lists, menus, itineraries, travel tickets, film/concert tickets, road signs, adverts, captions, tables, TV listings, restaurant reviews, instructions, medicine labels, brochures.
2. Experiment with the different fonts on a computer program.
3. Look at books in the library, taking note of different fonts, size of writing etc.

Homework suggestion

Pupils find different types of reading materials from home.

Recommended reading

Pupils read different types of poetry; e.g.

Whispers of love by Janis Priestley

Do you know my teacher?
(male and female version) by John Rice

Hippopotamus by Liz Brownlee

Waves by Jackie Kay

1 Read this poem about TV programmes.

> At half past three, it's my favourite soap
> At five past four, it's cartoons I hope.
>
> At four thirty-five, it's time for the match,
> And six-fifteen brings 'Marrow patch'.
>
> At twenty to seven it's the 'Pop hero' show,
> At quarter to eight, it's sun, rain or snow.
>
> A box office film starts at exactly eight,
> My homework will surely have to wait.

Be choosy about what you watch on the telly!

2 Write the TV programmes in a clearer way. You can make up names for some of the programmes and the TV channel.

Channel:		
Time	**Programme**	**Type**

3 Read a TV guide. Find and write the name of:

(a) a sports programme _____

(b) a factual programme _____

(c) a kid's programme _____

(d) a film _____

Objective

Engage with a wide variety of poetry and verse on a regular basis

Activities covered

- Naming something scary
- Reading a poem
- Answering questions about a poem
- Writing verse
- Performing a poem as a group

Background information

There are a great many exercises that can be done using poetry. Pupils should be exposed to different types of poetry, although too much serious poetry at a young age might put them off. Teachers should cater for different tastes and abilities. Poems should be age-appropriate. Pupils will develop a love of poetry if they are reading humorous, lighthearted and meaningful poems they can understand and relate to. Different forms of poetry such as haiku, sonnet, cinquain etc. should be explored too. Pupils may not like all the poems studied but that's OK! In this lesson, the topic is fear. The pupils should be understanding of others' fears, and not make fun of them.

Recommended reading

(scary)

Read to the class:

Ghoul school rules by Sue Cowling
The ghoul inspectre's coming by Liz Brownlee
Timetable by Julia Rawlinson
The evil genius by Philip Waddell
Bogeyman headmaster by John Agard

Before the lesson

Prepare different types of poetry to read to the pupils.

The lesson

1. The pupils name something that frightens them.
2. Read the poem as a class.
3. The pupils answer Questions 3 to 5. This exercise can be done individually or as a class.
4. The pupils write one verse in the same style as the example. They should then form groups of three or four and practise a performance of their poem, incorporating movement and expression. The poems can then be performed for the class.
5. To end the lesson, hold a class discussion about frightening situations.

Answers

1. – 2. Teacher check
3.   fear
4. – 8. Teacher check

Additional activities

Pupils can:

1. Explore and try different forms of poetry; e.g. concrete poetry, haiku, story-poem, nursery rhyme, chant, free verse, serious and humorous poetry.
2. Make a class collection of different types/forms of poems.
3. Read poetry by different poets. Research the poets.
4. Each write a different type of poem. These can be shared with the class and put together to form a class anthology.
5. Read a new poem each week.

1 Name something that scares you. _____

2 Read the poem below as a class.

> Fear makes the wolf bigger than he is.

I'm the ...

I'm the shadow on your wall,
I'm the eerie night wolf call,
And I'm everything to you except a friend.

I'm the thing under your bed,
I'm the monsters in your head,
And I'm waiting for you just around the bend.

I'm the ghost that you can sense,
I'm the forest dark and dense,
And I'm watching everything that you do.

I'm the warm breath in your ear,
And the vampire that is near,
I am fear and I am following you.

> What is a ghost's favourite game? Hide and shriek!

3 Who/What is speaking in the poem? _____

4 Circle on the poem the things you would find scary.

5 Write some frightening words.

6 Use your own words to write one verse of a scary poem in a similar style to the example.

I'm the _____

I'm the _____

And _____

7 Find two or three people to work with. Put your verses together and practise saying the whole poem aloud. Vary your movements, the number of people saying each line and your expression. Make it scary!

8 Present your poem to the class.

Scan it

Objective

Develop basic information retrieval skills

Activities covered

- Reading a poem as a class
- Reading a poem on own
- Answering questions without looking at information
- Checking answers
- Discussing a poem

Background information

Explain to the pupils what scanning or skimming a text entails. Scanning is reading a text quickly to obtain key words. Skimming is reading a text quickly to obtain a rough idea of the main points.

Before the lesson

The teacher could have other examples of text for the pupils to scan/skim read.

The lesson

1. Read the poem quickly as a class. No discussion of the poem should take place, although some of the words can be defined; e.g. 'feline', 'catastrophe', 'Monarch butterflies'.

2. The pupils read the poem to themselves quickly and quietly. A time limit could be set for this activity.

3. The pupils cover the poem and answer the questions. Check that no peeking takes place!

4. The pupils check their answers. This can be done as a class or individually.

5. The poem, any difficult words and how successful pupils were at scanning the text can be discussed as a class.

6. The pupils re-read the poem for enjoyment.

Answers

1. – 2. Teacher check

3. (a) Answers must include three of the following:
    seafood cake, roasted rats, mouse stew, milk, birds, kitty-cat crisps

    (b) a hunting video

    (c) by the fire

    (d) her child

    (e) yes

    (f) Answers must include two of the following:
    lick paws, flea spray, sharpen claws

    (g) Answers must include two of the following:
    watching video, sitting by the fire, catching butterflies, playing with balls of wool

    (h) They are trying to get the party ready and there is still a lot to be done. They are 'in a flap.'

4. Teacher check

Additional activities

Pupils can:

1. Scan/skim read in other subjects, such as history, and write keywords.

2. Scan homework notes, writing down just what helps them remember what they have to do.

3. Scan/skim read a passage and put this information into a table.

4. Scan recipes and make a shopping list for the ingredients.

5. Scan instructions and see what tools are needed.

6. Write a paragraph based on information in a table or chart.

7. Complete comprehension activities based on something that has been read.

8. Look at everyday reading material and answer questions on it; e.g. timetables, messages, emails, directions, weather maps.

If you scan a text, it means you read it quickly, taking note of the important points.

1 Read this poem quickly as a class.

Cat flap

'Now help me to get ready',
said Mummy cat to child,
'Our guests will soon be arriving,
this party should be wild!

Put out the seafood cake,
and carve the roasted rats,
add spices to the mouse stew,
and display balloons and hats.

Set out the saucers of milk,
arrange that platter of birds,
put on that hunting video,
this is not a do for nerds.

Put kitty-cat crisps in a bowl,
place some cushions by the fire,
let loose those Monarch butterflies,
we can play until we tire.

C'mon, hurry, they'll soon be here!
I still need to lick my paws,
and I must put my flea spray on,
and sharpen up my claws.

Have we put out the balls of wool?
What a busy night it will be!
I hope our feline friends have fun,
We don't want a catastrophe!'

2 Read it quickly and quietly to yourself. Form a picture in your head while you are reading—it will help you remember.

3 Cover the poem and answer the questions. **Do not peek!**

(a) Name three types of food that will be served.

_____

_____

_____

(b) What kind of video will be shown?

_____

(c) Where were the cushions placed?

_____

(d) Who was helping Mummy cat?

_____

(e) Did they have balloons?

_____

(f) Name two grooming routines Mummy cat has to do.

_____

_____

(g) Name two activities for the guests.

_____

_____

(h) Why do you think the poem is called 'Cat flap'?

_____

_____

4 Check your answers. How many did you get correct?

/₈

Date with a dictionary

Objective
Use simple dictionaries effectively

Activities covered
- Reading a poem
- Looking up words in a dictionary
- Writing a story

Background information
Each pupil should have his/her own dictionary to keep with him/her at all times. Pupils should be encouraged to use their dictionaries when they find a word they do not know or when they are completing a writing task.

Before the lesson
The pupils will need their own dictionary. Check that the words on the copymaster are in the pupils' dictionaries.

The lesson
1. The pupils read the poem.
2. The pupils look up meanings of words in a dictionary and write them.
3. The pupils write a short story using the words in the list. Full sentences should be used and the story must make sense. The story example given in the Answers below could be read aloud before the pupils begin writing. They may like to draft their story on scrap paper first.
4. The pupils open the dictionary to any page and find a word they do not know. (If they know all the words on that page, they can open it again.) They then write the new word and its meaning to answer Question 4.
5. The pupils can share these new words with the class, perhaps in the form of a guessing game.

Answers
1. Teacher check
2. (a) artist – person who produces works of art/ entertainer
   (b) masterpiece – excellent piece of work
   (c) realistic – seeing things as they are
   (d) portrait – picture of person/animal
   (e) dab – touch something quickly and gently
   (f) pride – to feel proud
   (g) ferocious – fierce or savage
   (h) ogre – giant/terrifying person.
3. Example (right)
4. Teacher check

There was an ***artist*** by the name of Harry. He was actually an ***ogre*** and everyone was terrified of him as they thought he was ***ferocious***. (Although he was actually very gentle.) One day, he decided to paint a ***portrait*** of himself. He kept looking at himself in the mirror and painted a dab of colour here and a ***dab*** of colour there. When he had finished, he looked at his work. He thought, 'This is not a ***realistic*** portrait of me, I look so handsome in the painting!' He looked in the mirror again only to find that he was indeed quite handsome! He was transformed! The painting was a ***masterpiece*** and Harry felt great ***pride***. He became a famous painter and a popular member of the community.

Additional activities
Pupils can:
1. Use dictionaries to look up words in other subjects; e.g. geography.
2. Play a dictionary game, in groups, where they look up a word in the dictionary as fast as they can.
3. Complete exercises about words in the dictionary; e.g. correct pronunciation and other information about each word.
4. Replace given words in a sentence with words that have a similar meaning, which have been found in the dictionary or a thesaurus.

Websites
(online dictionary and thesaurus)

<www.m-w.com>
<www.yourdictionary.com>
<http://dictionary.reference.com>

1 Read this poem.

Arty Art

Mmmm, what can I do on this rainy day?
Something to make Mum glad,
I know! I'll do a painting,
As an artist, I'm not bad!

I got all my stuff together,
And some paper, bright and white,
I started on my masterpiece,
And worked into the night.

I drew, I shaded, I coloured in,
I painted so perfectly,
I wanted it to be realistic,
This portrait done by me!

I added the finishing touches,
Colours dabbed here and there,
I handed it to my mother,
With utmost pride and care.

'Oh, my darling, that's excellent!
What a ferocious monster you drew!'
'Actually, Mum, that's no ogre,
it is a picture of you.'

The Spanish painter, Picasso, is said to have produced over 13 000 paintings!

2 Look these words up in a dictionary. Write their meanings.

(a) artist _____

_____

(b) masterpiece _____

_____

(c) realistic _____

_____

(d) portrait _____

_____

(e) dab _____

(f) pride _____

_____

(g) ferocious _____

_____

(h) ogre _____

_____

3 Plan a short story, using as many of the words in Question 2 as you can. Make it interesting! Use the back of the worksheet to write your story. Write rough notes here.

_____

_____

_____

_____

Read it to yourself. How many of the words did you use? _____

4 Open the dictionary to any page and find a word you do not know. Write the word and its meaning.

_____   _____

Take your time

Objective

Write regularly and gradually extend the period over which a writing effort is sustained

Activities covered

- Reading poem
- Underlining keywords in a poem
- Discussing a poem
- Researching information for a poem
- Writing keywords
- Starting a poem
- Checking and revising poem

Background information

The idea behind this lesson is that pupils continue adding to and improving their writing over a number of days or weeks. It is up to the teacher what the time limit is. Explain to the pupils that it will be up to them to complete it by the due date, during extra time in class or at home. Because the pupils have longer than usual to complete their poem, they should be improving it and adding to it until it is the best they can do. Research is an important part of writing this poem; therefore, the pupils must have access to resources if the topic has not already been discussed in class. Sufficient time must be allowed for research. The pupils' poems can take any form and need not rhyme.

Before the lesson

Decide how long the pupils have to complete the written task, and how long their finished poems should be.

Pupils will need to have researched a particular culture/country. The pupils should have access to information resources and enough time for the research. The teacher can stipulate which culture the pupils are to write about (e.g. what is being studied in another learning area) or may allow the pupils to choose their own.

The lesson

1. The pupils read the poem and underline keywords.
2. Discuss the poem as a class.
3. The pupils can now begin their research (if not a topic already covered in class) and write keywords concerning aspects of the culture.
4. The pupils start writing their poem. The poem can be in any form.
5. The pupils continue to write their poem in their own time on a separate sheet of paper.
6. The pupils check and add to their poem until they consider it to be ready. They can then add pictures, borders etc.
7. All poems can be put together in a booklet and/or displayed in the school.

Answers

1. – 6. Teacher check

Additional activity

Pupils can:

Write the following over a period of time: a class story, a fairytale, a poem with a specific format, a short play.

You will be given quite a bit of time to complete your poem, therefore you must keep checking it and improving it until it is the absolute best you can do!

1 Read this poem and underline the keywords.

> The San people are a tribe in Africa. The San people are famous for their cave paintings.

My people

My name is Kimbu and I belong to the San,
We gather our food and hunt when we can.

We like to eat nuts, wild berries and meat,
We track our dinner in the African heat.

Animal skins are our everyday dress,
We've nothing to prove and no-one to impress.

We are called nomads, always changing our space,
We pack up few belongings, hardly leaving a trace.

The Kalahari Desert is our neighbourhood,
Our homes made of leaves and branches of wood.

But now there are farms taking over the lands,
We'll have to stop moving, fate out of our hands.

The tribes will build villages, to a modern life tend,
The traditional San will come to an end.

Your keywords

2 Research and write your own poem about a different culture you are interested in. Which culture is your poem going to be about? _____

3 Do your research and write keywords in the box above.

> Your poem should have information about the people you researched.

4 Write the beginning of your poem in the space below.

_____

_____

_____

_____

5 Continue your poem on a separate sheet of paper and remember to check it and improve it! Remember to give your poem a title.

6 When you are satisfied with your work, write your poem out neatly and decorate it.

Button up

Objective

Experience varied and consistent oral language activity as a preparation for writing

Activities covered

- Answering questions about an imaginary person as a group
- Discussing a character
- Writing a four-line poem (clerihew)
- Assessing a four-line poem

Background information

Oral language precedes most writing activities. It gets pupils thinking about a topic and allows them to hear different viewpoints.

Before the lesson

Prepare a jar of different buttons. These should be as interesting as possible. Sewing and fabric shops will sell buttons at a reasonable price.

Divide the class into groups.

The lesson

1. Pass around the jar of buttons and have each group choose one. Each group then takes some time looking at their button and passing it around so that all group members can see it.
2. Read the questions with the class so they can see the aim of the questions.
3. The groups answer the questions about the button and the person who wore it. Answers do not have to be full sentences.
4. Still in groups, the pupils write a four-line poem about the character of this person. This can be a simple poem with an aabb rhyme scheme, or the teacher can show pupils how to write a clerihew, as shown below.
5. The pupils assess their poems by colouring buttons.
6. Poems can be displayed in the classroom or school with the button attached.

Answers

1. – 4. Teacher check

> **Clerihew:** 4 lines long
>
> 1st line   – 1st line names the person
> 2nd line   – 2nd line rhymes with person's name
> 3rd line   } rhyme
> 4th line
>
> (Usually humorous, but does not have to be for this lesson.)

Additional activities

Pupils can:

1. Write an article about an event that has happened at school, such as a visit from an important person, a sports day etc. Discussion should precede the writing.
2. Discuss safety and make a poster titled '10 Rules of Safety'. These should be displayed in the school.
3. Discuss caring for their environment. Each pupil can then make a poster about what he/she thinks is the most important thing to do to preserve the environment.
4. As a class, make up a story, with all pupils contributing to the story.
5. Discuss the news in the local area and write a news bulletin.
6. Discuss topics in other subjects and complete written tasks based on the discussion.

Button up

Let your imagination loose!

1 In a group, choose an old button. Pass the button around the group and look at it closely.

2 As a group, discuss the questions and decide the answers.

(a) What type of clothing did it come from? _____

(b) Describe what you think the clothing may have looked like (colour, condition, type, texture, fabric etc.).

> Make your answers interesting!

_____

_____

(c) Who was wearing the piece of clothing the button is from?

_____

_____

(d) What kind of person was he/she? _____

(e) Where was the person when he/she last wore it? _____

(f) What was he/she doing there? _____

(g) What are the person's favourite things? _____

_____

(h) What does he/she dislike? _____

(i) Briefly describe this person's character. _____

_____

(j) Where is the garment now? _____

_____

3 In your groups, write a four-line poem about the person you imagined.

_____

_____

_____

_____

4 What do you think of your poem? Colour the buttons (5 = wow! 1 = oh-oh!).

Button up!

Use questions

Objective

Learn to use questions as a mechanism for expanding and developing a poem

Activities covered

- Choosing a nursery rhyme to write about
- Writing a poem
- Reading a poem to self
- Writing a descriptive paragraph
- Self-assessing a descriptive paragraph and a poem

Background information

Pupils should be encouraged to ask questions when they are writing stories, poems, sentences, paragraphs, or just about anything. The basic 'question' words who, where, when, why, what and how, should be permanently displayed in the classroom to remind the pupils. They should use these questions to add more details to their writing.

Before the lesson

A list of nursery rhymes could be prepared, if necessary.

The lesson

1. Discuss nursery rhymes with the pupils, reciting some examples.
2. Each pupil chooses a nursery rhyme.
3. The pupils turn their chosen nursery rhyme into a poem by asking themselves questions. The example provided should be discussed first. Another example could be modelled with the whole class to make sure that all pupils understand. The pupils should use rhyme in their poems if possible.
4. The pupils read their poem to themselves, then write a descriptive paragraph about the characters in their poem. More details should be added.
5. The pupils comment on their paragraph and poem by asking the basic questions.

Answers

1. – 6. Teacher check

Additional activities

Pupils can:

1. Expand given sentences by asking questions.
2. Read a short story and discuss how the basic questions were answered.
3. Write a newspaper article about something that has occurred in the local community, making sure that all questions have been answered.
4. Write/Have a conversation using all the question words.
5. Make an advertisement for a holiday destination, ensuring all questions are answered.

Website

(nursery rhymes)

<http://www.rhymes.org.uk>

When you write a story or poem, you should ask yourself basic questions, such as
who?, what?, when?, why?, where? *and* **how**?

1 Choose a nursery rhyme you know well. _____

2 Read the example below. Look carefully at the questions.

> Rhyme: .... **Little Bo Peep**
>
> Who? .... *Little Bo Peep*
>
> Where? ....*In an empty field*
>
> When? .... *On a Sunday night*
>
> Why? ....*She's lost her sheep*
>
> What? .... *The entire flock*
>
> How? .... *While kissing Tony Knight.*

The rhyme, '**Baa baa black sheep**' is over 200 years old! That's even older than your teacher!

Use rhyming words if you can.

3 Write a poem for your chosen nursery rhyme.

Ask yourself:

Rhyme: _____

Who? _____

Where? _____

When? _____

Why? _____

What? _____

How? _____

4 Read your poem to yourself, without the question words.

5 Write a descriptive paragraph about the character(s) in your nursery rhyme. Use the ideas from your poem and add more details if you can.

Use full sentences!

6 Comment on

(a) your poem: _____

(b) your paragraph: _____

Objective

Give sequence to ideas and events in poems

Activities covered

- Writing morning activities in sequence
- Reading a poem
- Placing activities in order
- Writing a list of events from a fairytale in order

Background information

Pupils need to be able to sequence the ideas and events in stories and poems they read, and will in turn then be able to sequence their own written tasks.

Before the lesson

Give the pupils other examples of sequences; e.g. writing a project, making breakfast, getting ready to go out, tidying a bedroom.

The lesson

1. The pupils write their morning activities in sequence to complete Question 1.
2. Read the poem **Visitor** as a class.
3. The pupils number the activities in order as they appeared in the poem.
4. The pupils choose a well-known fairytale and write the events in the story in sequence. The whole story does not have to be written down – just the main events.
5. Discuss Questions 1, 3 and 4 as a class.

Answers

1. – 2. Teacher check
3. 10, 4, 2, 7, 9, 3, 6, 1, 5, 8
4. Teacher check

Additional activity

Pupils can:

Write events in time order for the following: a school event, a special day, how to write a story, preparing for a camping trip, making a school lunch box.

Website

<www.ability.org.uk/kids_recipe.html>

Think carefully about six things you did this morning before you came to school.

1 Write them in the order you did them.

_____

_____

_____

_____

_____

_____

2 Read the poem below.

> There should always be ORDER in the classroom!

Visitor

'We have not time to waste', said Mum.
'Granny is coming to stay.
This house must look so perfect,
She'll have nothing bad to say.'

For a week, we slaved to get it clean,
We overhauled each room.
As G-Day grew much closer,
We felt impending doom.

We banished spiders and their homes,
We polished all the doors,
We vacuumed behind the furniture,
And mopped and preened the floors.

We scrubbed between each bathroom tile,
The taps we made them shine,
Towels we fluffed and walls we buffed,
The house looked mighty fine.

Dad jazzed up the garden,
He even mowed the lawn,
He cleaned the bench so Gran could sit,
When she felt tired and worn.

'Your house looks quite neat and clean', said Gran.
'I hope you didn't go out of your way.'
Mum said sweetly, 'Ah, not at all,
It looks like this every day'.

3 Write the numbers 1–10 next to these activities to show the order in which they were done.

Mowed the grass...................... ☐

Mopped floors .... ☐

Polished doors .... ☐

Fluffed towels .... ☐

Jazzed up the garden .... ☐

Vacuumed .... ☐

Shined the taps....................... ☐

Dusted cobwebs .... ☐

Scrubbed bathroom .... ☐

Cleaned walls.......................... ☐

4 Choose a well-known fairytale. Write a list of main events in the order that they happened:

Fairytale: _____

_____

_____

_____

_____

_____

Who is reading it?

Objective

Develop an appreciation of how the intended audience should influence the nature of a piece of writing

Activities covered

- Selecting and writing for a target audience
- Writing a two-line poem for an advertisement
- Checking own advertisement
- Assessing own advertisement

Background information

Pupils should become aware that who they are writing for should influence how they write and how their work is presented. They need to be able to see examples of how specific audiences are targeted.

Before the lesson

Prepare many examples of texts and objects that have targeted specific audiences; e.g. books, advertisements, films, newspapers, product labels, TV programmes, cards, magazines, toys, games.

The lesson

1. Discuss the prepared examples as a class. Identify the intended audience and how we know this; e.g. language used, colours, illustrations, interests, message.
2. The pupils decide who the two advertisements are intended for to answer Questions 1 and 2.
3. The pupils write a two-line advertisement for a food, deciding first who their audience is, and then targeting this specific audience to answer Question 3.
4. The pupils draft their advertisement using their created rhyme.
5. The pupils check their advertisement, to decide whether or not it suits the intended audience. They can then make any necessary improvements and rewrite it neatly.
6. All advertisements can be displayed in an appropriate part of the school. The class can look at the advertisements and decide who their audience would be. The writer of the advert will then see if he/she has targeted his/her audience accurately.
7. The pupils assess their advertisements by colouring the sweets.

Answers

1. – 6. Teacher check

Additional activities

Pupils can:

1. Write stories or poems for younger classes.
2. Write to a visitor coming to the school.
3. Write thank you letters to someone who has helped the school or community.
4. Present different factual information from other subjects, targeting a particular audience.
5. Write greeting cards for different people; e.g. grandparent, headteacher, friend, prime minister, famous sporting star.
6. Design different products for different audiences.

We need to vary our writing depending on who we are writing for.
For example, if you wrote a letter to a politician it would be very
different from one you would write to a friend.

1 What age group do you think this advertisement would be suitable for?

2 What age group do you think this advertisement is aimed at?

_____

Sweet toffees you can chew,
Delicious and brand new!

Silky, creamy toffee as an after-dinner treat,

A luxurious sensation you simply cannot beat.

3 Write a two-line rhyming poem for an advertisement for a different food.

_____

_____

Think about your advert!

• Who is your audience? _____

• How will you make the advertisement suitable for (or appealing to) your audience?

_____

_____

_____

4 Write your advertisement in draft form below, using your two-line poem.

5 Check your advertisement and improve it if you can. Rewrite it neatly on a separate sheet of paper and display it in the classroom.

6 Assess your advertisement by giving it a score out of 3.

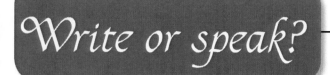

Objective

Develop an awareness of the difference between written language and oral language

Activities covered

- Reading a poem
- Writing a list
- Deciding, with a partner, whether oral or written language is more appropriate in different situations
- Turning oral language into written language

Background information

Pupils should know the difference between oral and written language and understand that one may be more effective than the other, depending on the situation.

Before the lesson

Prepare examples of when oral/written language is more effective. Examples could include news of the day, jokes, TV guides, saying thank you, apologising, timetables, invitations, advertisements, slogans.

The class will need to be divided into pairs.

The lesson

1. Discuss the differences between oral language and written language with the class. Give examples and have the pupils decide whether oral language or written language is more appropriate or whether it does not matter.
2. Read the poem *List* as a class. Any difficult words or terms can be discussed, such as 'herbal' and 'pastry'.
3. The pupils read the poem again and write a list that the mother may have written.
4. In pairs, the pupils take turns to be the mother.
5. Pupils decide which form of language would be better.
6. Pupils change oral language into written language.

Answers

1. Teacher check
2. List: bread, milk, ham, cheddar cheese, sardines, peas, teabags, hake (3), apples (6), flour
3. – 5. Teacher check
6. 'To Do List': Make bed, put clothes in laundry, take plates to the kitchen, find the rat

Additional activities

Pupils can:

1. Turn the following into oral language: a newspaper article, an advertisement in a magazine, a letter, instructions.
2. Turn the following into written language: a news bulletin, a conversation, a request for information, a complaint.

Recommended reading

(lists)

Two lists by Tony Bradman

Dr D Rision's shopping list by Sue Cowling

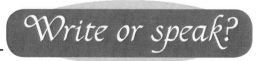

Depending on the situation, we sometimes use oral language (speaking) while at other times we may use written language.

1 Read the poem below.

List

Mum gave me a shopping list,
to get a few things at the store,
she said I must get only those,
and absolutely nothing more!

On the list was bread and milk,
some ham and cheddar cheese,
a tin of sardines in olive oil,
and frozen garden peas.

A box of herbal teabags,
three small pieces of hake,
six green Granny Smith apples,
and flour to bake a cake.

There was no bread, I bought some crisps,
no ham or cheese, bought sweets,
instead of sardines and yucky peas,
I bought the dog some treats.

No hake, so it was vanilla ice-cream,
no apples, no flour, no tea,
I bought instead toffees and cake,
Mum will be proud of me!

2 Write the list the poet's Mum might have written. Keep it simple!

_____

_____

_____

_____

_____

_____

_____

_____

_____

3 In pairs, take turns to be Mum and say the list. Do not read it from the poem!

4 In this case, which is better?

oral ☐   written ☐

5 Still in pairs, tick which form of communication would be more suitable in each situation.

	Oral language	Written language	Either
Menu			
Job interview			
Invitation			
School report			

6 Write a 'To do list' for this child.

Your room is a disgrace! I want you to make your bed, neatly, and pick all those clothes up off the floor! There are even plates under your bed! Did you notice that your rat Basil has escaped from its cage? It is running around your room somewhere! Just find him! Do these things right now!!

To do list

_____

_____

_____

_____

_____

_____

Check it carefully

Objective

Learn to revise and redraft writing

Activities covered

- Singing a song
- Singing different version of a song
- Writing own words for song
- Redrafting and rewriting work
- Reading work to a partner and following suggestions

Background information

Pupils should be revising and redrafting their work on a constant basis. It is something that should be part of their writing routine. The teacher should afford specific time to allow pupils to check and revise their work, and there should be no discussion or talking allowed during this time. Pupils will soon develop good habits and automatically check through written work they have done.

Before the lesson

The class will be divided into pairs.

The lesson

1. The teacher can discuss with the class what revising and redrafting work means.
2. The class sings *'My bonnie lies over the ocean'*.
3. Pupils sing the same tune using the words on the worksheet.
4. Pupils write their own words to match the tune.
5. Pupils read their song to themselves and redraft their writing, making improvements if they can. Pupils check their rhyme, rhythm and spelling.
6. Pupils read/sing their song to their partner. Partners can make suggestions if they think it can be improved upon. Pupils then amend it if they agree with the suggestions.
7. Pupils repeat the activity on the back of the worksheet.
8. Songs can be displayed in the classroom and a few of them can be sung together as a class.

Answers

1. – 7. Teacher check

Additional activities

Pupils can:

1. Check each other's work and redraft writing tasks.
2. Write projects for other subjects and then redraft after checking with the teacher.

Other examples:

My poodle lies under my duvet,
My poodle lies on my armchair,
My poodle lies stretched on my clothing,
Oh why am I covered in hair?

or

My teacher has gone to Tobago,
My teacher has gone to Peru,
My teacher has gone to Hawaii,
To get away from me and you.

Always check your work to make sure there are no mistakes!

1 As a class, sing the song 'My bonnie lies over the ocean'.

2 Sing it again, using these words:

> *My homework lies under the table,*
> *My homework lies under my bed,*
> *My homework lies inside my schoolbag,*
> *I think I'll watch TV instead.*
>
> *I think, oh I think, I think I'll watch TV instead, instead.*
> *I think, oh I think, I think I'll watch TV instead.*

> Notice how the first three lines start the same way. Yours should do the same!

3 Make up your own words for this song. Try to keep the rhythm and meter the same as the original.

_____

_____

_____

_____

_____

_____

4 Read your song to yourself. Redraft it, improving it if you can. Make sure your rhyme and rhythm are correct. Check your spelling too!

5 Read it (or sing it if you are really brave) to a partner. If your partner has any good suggestions, follow them!

6 Give yourself a star rating for your song.

OK   Good   Excellent

7 On the back of this worksheet, write another set of words to match the song.

You shouldn't have

Objective

Learn to use a wider range of punctuation marks with greater accuracy as part of the revision and editing process

Activities covered

- Correcting sentences
- Writing sentences
- Reading a poem
- Circling punctuation marks
- Writing a poem
- Reading poem

Background information

Pupils of this age should be using full stops, commas, exclamation marks, question marks and apostrophes correctly as part of their writing. They also need to be made aware of them in their reading from time to time. Different punctuation marks could be displayed on charts in the classroom.

Before the lesson

Prepare examples of different punctuation marks.

The lesson

1. Discuss punctuation marks with the class and show the prepared examples of punctuation marks.
2. The pupils correct two sentences to complete Question 1.
3. The pupils write a sentence that includes each punctuation mark to answer Question 2.
4. Read the poem *'I should not have!'* as a class. Point out the punctuation marks and the reasons for using them. Read the poem again, taking note of the punctuation marks.
5. The pupils write their own 'I should not have...' poem, using the same format as the example. They must use correct punctuation and full sentences.
6. The pupils read their poem to themselves, making sure that the punctuation is correct.

Answers

1. (a) There is a lion, leopard and tiger behind you!
   (b) Can you give me directions to Hillrock Kennels? I want to visit my poodle.
2. – 5. Teacher check

Additional activities

Pupils can:

1. Take note of punctuation marks in class readers.
2. Write a four- or five-line poem on a given topic, using a different punctuation mark on each line.
3. Display a checklist in the classroom for the editing process.

Homework suggestion

Have the pupils find a passage from a magazine or newspaper, cut it out and glue it on a sheet of paper. The pupils then write labels to show the different punctuation marks. The passages can be read the following day in class.

You shouldn't have

Punctuation marks help make sense of what we read.

1 The punctuation marks in the sentences below are incorrect. Rewrite the sentences correctly.

(a) there is a lion. leopard and tiger behind you?

_____

(b) can you give me directions to hillrock kennels! i want to visit, my poodle?

_____

_____

2 Write a sentence using each punctuation mark:

(a) . _____

(b) , _____

(c) ? _____

(d) ! _____

3 Read the poem below. Circle the punctuation marks.

> You would never do these things!

I should not have!

I should not have given my peas to the cat,
or called your friend's daughter a mean, ugly brat.

I should not have left pizza under my bed,
or tried to set fire to the garden shed.

I should not have painted the grand piano white,
or tied my sister to the tree so tight.

I should not have thrown my homework away,
or invited those bikers to come over and stay.

I should not have told Miss Smith to get lost,
or phoned friends in China, regardless of cost.

I should not have done all those things that I did!
You have to forgive me as I'm only a kid.

4 On a separate sheet of paper, write a poem of your own with the title 'I should not have!' Try to make it rhyme. Use correct punctuation!

5 Read your poem to yourself. Take note of your punctuation marks when you are reading!

Poetry skills   **65**

Write to something

Objective

Learn to write with increasing grammatical accuracy through the process of revision and editing

Activities covered

- Reading a letter poem
- Writing a letter to something or someone
- Using a checklist to edit a poem
- Correcting mistakes in a poem
- Rewriting a poem after editing

Background information

Pupils need to get into the practice of thoroughly checking and revising their own work. This is not something that comes naturally to most pupils, as they are usually keen to get the task finished as quickly as possible! The pupils should be shown a systematic guide on how to revise and edit their own work. This can be in the form of a checklist that can be displayed in the classroom. Specific time should be allocated for the pupils to check their work and the class should be silent during checking times.

Recommended reading

(letters)

Letters to the three pigs by Clare Bevan

Love letter by Alison Chisholm

Postcard from the edge by Jane Wright

Letter from a super villain's mum by Paul Cookson

Before the lesson

Display a checklist in the classroom for revising and editing written work.

The lesson

1. Explain to class what editing and revising their work entails.
2. As a class read the poem **'To my reading book'**.
3. The pupils choose someone or something to write to and write a letter. The letter can also be from anyone or anything. So that it is in the form of a poem, each new sentence should start on a new line.
4. The pupils edit and revise their poem using the checklist provided, ticking each when they have checked that aspect.
5. The pupils correct any mistakes in their poems.
6. The pupils rewrite their poems. These can be displayed in the classroom so the pupils can read each other's work.

Answers

1. – 5. Teacher check

Additional activities

Pupils can:

1. Edit and correct peer work.
2. Write sentences and edit them with the help of a teacher or classmate.
3. Use new grammar they have learnt in their own writing.
4. Write pieces for display, making sure grammar and spelling are correct.

Homework suggestion

Have the pupils write a note to a type of food they do not like. They should revise and edit their work, making sure grammar and spelling are correct. These can then be displayed in the classroom.

1 Read the letter below.

> ### To my reading book
>
> *Now listen here, book, it's you I must read,*
> *And I don't feel like doing this nasty deed.*
>
> *Please be interesting, funny and smart,*
> *Grab my attention, right from the start.*
>
> *I could have left you on the library shelf,*
> *I picked you out of hundreds, all by myself.*
>
> *I hope that your words are simple and few,*
> *For tomorrow I must hand in my book review.*
>
> ### From Reluctant Reader

2 Write your own letter using a similar format. It can be to anyone or anything in your life. It can be to a toy, your cat, the neighbour, your fridge, or anything you like! The lines do not have to rhyme.

> Start each sentence on a new line so that it's like a poem!

To: _____

_____

_____

_____

_____

_____

_____

_____

_____

From: _____

3 Check your poem carefully! Use the checklist below.

Check these

☐ Capital letters for names

☐ Capital letters at the beginning of sentences

☐ Full stops at the end of sentences

☐ Full sentences

☐ Commas (if necessary)

☐ Spelling

☐ Correct grammar

4 Correct any mistakes.

5 Rewrite your letter neatly on a separate sheet of paper.

Spell it out

Objective

Use a range of aids and strategies, including the use of approximate spelling, to improve his/her command of spelling

Activities covered

- Trying to spell words correctly
- Discussing how different words are spelt
- Identifying spelling mistakes in a poem
- Correcting spelling mistakes
- Writing similar words
- Spelling difficult words

Background information

Pupils should not feel daunted by words they cannot spell, but instead, use a range of strategies in attempting to spell them. Strategies include breaking the word up into recognisable parts, looking at prefixes and suffixes as well as the root word, or deciding if the word is similar to another word that they know. Pupils can also look at letter strings or patterns. Pupils should be praised for efforts made even if they do not get the spelling perfectly correct.

Before the lesson

Prepare a challenging list of 10 words to read to the pupils for Question 1. Alternatively, the following list could be used: 'potatoes', 'breakfast', 'thundering', 'dangerous', 'difficult', 'friendly', 'hurried', 'complained', 'detective', 'conversation'.

The pupils will require dictionaries.

The lesson

1. Discuss several strategies the class could use when spelling words. Several examples can be done together as a class.

2. Read out 10 words for the pupils to spell. (See 'Before the lesson'.) The pupils try to spell each word correctly to complete Question 1.

3. The answers to Question 1 are discussed as a class. Each word is studied and pulled apart. The pupils can identify words that are similar, or mention prefixes and suffixes, word parts or letter strings and patterns.

4. The pupils read the poem *'Camel'* and underline the spelling mistakes. There are 10 mistakes.

5. The pupils attempt to spell the words correctly. This exercise can be done individually.

6. The pupils write a word that is similar in some way to the word they have written to complete Question 3. The poem and spelling mistakes are discussed as a class.

7. The pupils find a difficult word in a dictionary and challenge a partner to spell it. The chosen words can then be discussed, along with any strategies the pupils used to try to spell them correctly.

Answers

1. – 2. Teacher check

3. interesting, moisture, eyelashes, breath, kisses, back, water, think, desert, luggage.

   Words that are in some way similar may include the following examples: interesting – any 'ing' words; moisture – moist, hoist, structure, adventure; eyelashes – sash/sashes, mashes, washes; breath – breathe, bread; kisses – misses, hisses; back – black, sack, track; water – porter, war; think – blink, this, drink; desert – Bert, desire; luggage – baggage

Additional activities

Pupils can:

1. Complete spelling exercises frequently, focusing on one or two word parts at a time.

2. Read aloud from a class reading book and take note of spellings and spelling patterns.

3. Complete a weekly spelling test. This can be informal and use words that have familiar prefixes/suffixes/word parts or words the pupils have come across during that week.

4. Play spelling games in groups.

Homework suggestion

A family member can give each pupil 10 spelling words to write. These are then checked as a class.

Even if you do not know how to spell a word, you should always try!

1 Your teacher will read some words to you. Write each one even if you are not sure of the spelling.

_____

_____

_____

_____

_____

_____

_____

_____

_____

2 Discuss the words as a class.

3 The poem below contains some spelling mistakes. Underline the mistakes and correct them in the box below. Next to each word, write a word you know that is similar in some way.

Camel

Now the camel is an intresting lass,
Who can take the heat of the sun.
She sweats very little to keep moistcha in,
Deodorant she needs none!

She can bat her eyelashs at you,
She has two rows you see,
She's reported to have very bad breth,
From her kisess you must flee.

She's one or two bumps on her bak,
That's all made up of fat,
That can turn food into warter,
Now what do you tink of that?

She's known as the ship of the dessert,
She'll carry your luggig and you,
So when you visit the arid lands,
Will it be one hump or two?

> The camel's nostrils can close up completely to block out sand.

Spelling corrections	Similar words
_____	_____
_____	_____
_____	_____
_____	_____
_____	_____
_____	_____
_____	_____
_____	_____

Objective

Develop his/her ability to write using information technology

Activities covered

- Reading a love poem
- Writing a love poem
- Rating a poem
- Completing a sentence
- Typing and displaying a poem

Background information

This lesson gives pupils the opportunity to 'typeset' their work and print it out. Pupils should be doing this regularly. It will give them more confidence using computers and the presentation of their work will be of a higher standard. This particular lesson would be ideal for Valentine's Day. If possible, the pupils can search for copyright-free images on the Internet to go with their poems. If this is not possible, they should have access to some form of clipart on the computer. The pupils will need to have some knowledge of 'copy and paste' to complete this task.

Before the lesson

Prepare examples of other love poems to show the class.

The pupils will need to have access to the Internet to look for copyright-free pictures. Alternatively, the pupils can use clipart available on the computer. They should have some knowledge of how to 'copy and paste' the pictures.

All pupils will need to have access to a computer to 'typeset' their poems and add pictures; therefore, this lesson can be taken over a few days.

The lesson

1. Read the poem as a class. Point out the rhyme pattern as the pupils will have to use it for their own poems.
2. The pupils write their own love poem, following the example. The rhyme pattern must be the same. The pupils can look for pictures on the Internet to go with their poem or use clipart.
3. The pupils give their poem a score out of five to complete Question 3.
4. The pupils complete the sentence: 'Love is …' to complete Question 5.
5. The pupils type and print out their work, add pictures they have found and display their love poems in the classroom/school.

Answers

1. – 5. Teacher check

Additional activities

Pupils can:

1. Use the Internet to find formulas for writing different types of poems; e.g. cinquain, concrete poetry, tanka.
2. Make use of online dictionaries.
3. Look up websites for schools and read projects/poetry/stories that other pupils have written.
4. Use the Internet to look up facts for a project.
5. Play online language games.

1 Read the love poem below.

I love you

I love you lots,

I love you stacks,

My love for you would fill ten sacks,

Twenty dustbins,

Fifty-five mugs,

Fourteen swimming pools,

And eight milk jugs.

2 Write a poem using the same format.

I love you _____

I love you _____

My love for you would _____

_____

_____

_____

_____

> Try to keep the rhyme scheme the same!

3 How romantic is your poem? Give it a romance score out of 5 by colouring the hearts.

4 Type your love poem, print it out and display it for the rest of the class. Find pictures on the Internet or computer to go with your poem. Of course, you do not have to say for whom it is written!

> Love me, love my dog.

5 Complete the sentence.

Love is _____

_____

Choose it yourself

Objective

Write a poem about a special place

Activities covered

- Drawing a chosen place
- Reading a poem
- Writing a poem
- Taking out parts of a poem
- Reading own poem and commenting on it
- Reading own poem to the class

Background information

Pupils should be given the chance to select their own topics when writing stories, poems, projects, letters, or any other writing task. Allowing them to select their own topics means that they will choose a topic that interests them, which should motivate them to write.

Before the lesson

An example of a similar poem could be shared with the class.

Soft music could be played in the background while the pupils are writing.

The lesson

1. Have the pupils think about places that are special to them. Allow them a few minutes to decide what place they are going to draw and write about.

2. Discuss the format of the poem *'Africa'*.

3. The pupils draw their chosen place in detail to complete Question 1. There should be no discussion allowed at this point so the pupils can completely focus on the task. Soft music can be played as the pupils draw.

4. The pupils write a poem about the place they drew, following the example.

5. The pupils remove certain words from the poem, as in the example. They should rewrite the modified poem on a separate sheet of paper.

6. The pupils read their own poem to themselves and comment on it.

7. The pupils display their poem. They can also read it to the class.

Answers

1. – 5. Teacher check

Additional activity

Pupils can:

Choose their own topics when writing projects, poems, stories, dialogues, sentences, letters etc.

Choose a place that is special to you.

1 Draw it in detail.

2 (a) Read the example below.

> *Of course you cannot usually taste a place! Use your imagination!*

Africa

I see .... trees **in an arid landscape**

I smell .... the **sweet grass**

I hear .... the **distant call of a hyena**

I feel .... the **wilderness touching**

I taste .... the **fear of something near**

I think .... **I don't belong here**

(b) Write your poem about your special place.

Title: _____

I see _____

I smell _____

I hear _____

I feel _____

I taste _____

I think _____

> IMAGINE this place!

3 Take away the 'I see', 'I smell' etc. and rewrite the poem on a separate sheet of paper. In the example, the words in bold are the poem.

4 Read your poem to yourself. What do you think of your poem?

_____

5 Read your poem to the class or display it in the classroom.

 *Just for you*

Objective

Choose to write for himself/herself only

Activities covered

- Completing sentences to create poem
- Reading a poem to self
- Assessing ease of writing
- Giving reasons for an answer

Background information

Pupils are always writing for the teacher or others, so this gives them the opportunity to write just for themselves. The lesson is all about them—it is a time for them to reflect on themselves and write about who they are. It is entirely up to them whether they wish to share their poem with others or not.

Before the lesson

Provide examples of poems where people have written about themselves.

The lesson

1. Explain to the class that this lesson is to give everyone the chance to write about themselves. It is a good idea to mention to the pupils at the beginning of the lesson that they do not have to share their work. This will give some pupils more freedom in their writing. The pupils should be encouraged to write positively about themselves.

2. Read through the unfinished sentences in Question 1. The pupils complete the poem by finishing the sentences. They should not be discussing their work with others at all. It is a personal poem and they should be focused on their writing task. Each line should be a full sentence with a full stop at the end. The pupils must add more than one word for each line, giving as much detail as space allows.

3. The pupils read the poem to themselves. They may decide to share their poem with a partner or the class. They can then comment on how easy it was to write about themselves.

4. The pupils can then put their poems safely away – for their eyes only!

Answers

1. – 3. Teacher check

Additional activities

Pupils can:

1. Keep a diary.
2. Write a to-do list for themselves of chores/activities they have to do every day.
3. Write a daily timetable for themselves.
4. Make a birthday list of friends'/family's birthdays.
5. Write out song lyrics.
6. Write a list of things to achieve and keep this somewhere safe.
7. Write any problems they may have, and possible solutions.
8. Design and make party invitations.
9. Design and make book covers, writing something relevant about the book's subject.

This activity is all about you. It will give you a chance to think about yourself! Be honest but say nice things!

1 Complete the sentences to make a poem about you.

I am _____

I wonder _____

I hear _____

I see _____

I want _____

I am _____

I pretend _____

I feel _____

I touch _____

I worry _____

I cry _____

I am _____

I understand _____

I say _____

I dream _____

I try _____

I hope _____

I am _____

2 Read your poem to yourself. It is entirely up to you if you want to share it with others. If you do not, put it safely away.

3 (a) How difficult was it to write about yourself?

Easy	OK	Difficult

(b) Give a reason for your answer. _____

_____

Who is it for?

Objective

Decide, after conferring with the teacher and others, who the audience for a piece of writing should be

Activities covered

- Writing a poem with a given format
- Checking a poem and improving it
- Reading a poem to a partner
- Deciding on an audience for a partner's poem
- Rewriting a poem to improve it

Background information

At this age, pupils should start to become more aware of the audience they are writing for. Different aspects of the writing need to be taken into consideration, such as wording, illustration, language used, content, font, size of letters, style of writing etc. Ideas such as these can be written on the board as a checklist for pupils, to make sure that all aspects of their poem are concentrated on targeting their specific audience.

Before the lesson

Divide the class into pairs.

The lesson

1. Explain the format of the poem provided. A few other examples can be done orally as a class.
2. The pupils write their own poem to complete Question 2, after choosing a target age group.
3. The pupils check their poem and improve on it if they can.
4. The pupils read their poem to their partner. The partner decides for which age group the poem would be best suited and gives reasons. Each pupil then states whether they agree with their partner or not. The pupils can change their age group if they wish based on their answers to Question 4.
5. The pupils discuss in pairs how they could best present their poem, targeting their specific age group.
6. The pupils rewrite their poem on a separate sheet of paper and decorate it according to the audience they are targeting.
7. Display the pupils' poems in the school so that their particular age groups can read them.

Answers

1. – 6. Teacher check

Additional activities

Pupils can:

1. Write titles and design front covers for books. The class discusses these and decides who the audience may be.
2. Design and write an invitation, ensuring it is suited to its recipient.
3. Make up a name and advertisements for a chocolate bar, targeting a specific audience.
4. Write a title and brief description for a new TV programme/film, deciding who the audience will be.

Homework suggestion

Study a written text found at home. Say who the intended audience is and how that can be determined.

For this lesson, choose an age group you want to write for.

1 Choose an age group you would like to write a poem for. Use the same format as the example below.

Choose any activity for the title.

Write three things that do this.

Write two describing words.

Write a simile; e.g. like a ... .

Singing

birds, Britney, Beatles

joyful, catchy

like a dad in the shower

Think of the age group you are writing for!

2 Write your poem in the space below.

_____

_____

_____

_____

3 Check your poem and improve it if you can.

4 (a) Read your poem to a partner. Ask him/her to tick the age group to which he/she thinks it is best suited. He/She should give you reasons.

0–3 years ....☐

4–7 years ....☐

8–12 years ....☐

12 years and older...☐

(b) Write one of your partner's reasons for choosing this age group.

_____

(c) Do you agree with your partner? Say why/why not.

_____

5 Consider your answers to Question 4 and change the age group if you wish. Discuss with your partner how you could present your poem so that it suits your age group better.

6 Rewrite your poem on a separate sheet of paper and decorate it to suit your audience.

Objective

Decide the quality of presentation in relation to the purpose and audience of a piece of writing

Activities covered

- Reading an example of a poetry format
- Writing a season poem
- Reading own poem to self
- Improving own poem
- Rewriting and decorating a poem

Background information

Pupils need to decide on the quality of their work based on the purpose of their writing. If they are writing a piece in draft form, it needn't be neat, whereas if they are writing for display, the work needs to have as a few mistakes as possible and the presentation also has to be of a good standard. The pupils should consider the purpose of their writing task, as well as their audience. The pupils should read their own work, improve on it, rewrite it, and decorate it.

Before the lesson

Decide for whom these poems will be displayed; e.g. for parents.

The lesson

1. Read the sample poem provided. The class can then write another example together on the board. Encourage the pupils to be as descriptive as possible.
2. Explain to the class where and how their writing will be displayed.
3. The pupils write a poem about a month or season. There should be no discussion allowed while the pupils are writing so they are completely focusing on the task.
4. The pupils read their poem to themselves, and improve it.
5. The pupils rewrite their poem and decorate it.
6. All poems should be displayed.

Answers

1. – 3. Teacher check

Additional activities

Pupils can:

1. Write for different audiences, such as family members, guests, classmates, teacher, penpal, school newspaper etc. The pupils should decide how the written task will be presented according to the audience it is aimed at.
2. Write for different purposes, such as poetry/writing competitions, website, projects, portfolios, class anthologies, play, advertising, pair or group work etc.

The poem you write will be displayed in the school for others to see.
Make sure your poem is well presented!

1 Read the example below. Look at the format.

> Cold hands, warm heart.

| (a) Choose a month or season. |

| (b) Picture how it would arrive if it were a person/animal. |

| (c) Add a few more words about its arrival. |

| (d) What does it do while it is here? |

| (e) How does it leave? |

> ### Winter
>
> *He strides in confidently,*
>
> | *taking big steps,* |
> | *sure-footed and proud.* |
>
> *He runs his icy fingers along*
> *the countryside,*
>
> | *and then finally turns his back* |
> | *on the bleakness and leaves,* |
> | *before the blossoms blind him.* |

> **Did you know?**
> Most snow crystals have six sides.

2 It's your turn to try to write a poem using the same format! Use some of the words in the word bank to help you if you wish.

(a) _____
Choose a month or season.

(b) _____
Picture how it would arrive if it were a person/animal.

(c) _____
Add a few more words about its arrival.

(d) _____
What does it do while it is here?

(e) _____
How does it leave?

Word bank

march, stagger, skip, float, tiptoe, gallop, hop, limp, hobble, wobble, sneak, zoom, tramp, dance, shuffle, glide, flutter, creep, stumble, trot, strut, slide, skate, leap, crawl, bounce, trudge, plod, slip, scurry, slink, prance

---

3 Read your poem to yourself and decide if you can improve it. Rewrite or type it and decorate it. Then display it!

Objective

Cooperate in writing a record of class activities

Activities covered

- Discussing the topic of school
- Writing an alphabet poem as a group
- Reading poems
- Putting poems together to make one poem
- Writing favourite rhyming couplets

Background information

It is good for the pupils to cooperate in writing a piece together. It gives them the opportunity to listen to others and accept different ideas and viewpoints. In this lesson, the pupils write first in groups, then put all their work together as a class. Check that all members in the group are contributing to the poem.

Before the lesson

Divide the class into groups. Each group must receive eight letters of the alphabet in consecutive order. The number of letters each group is given should be an even number so that pupils can use rhyming couplets.

The pupils must have a knowledge of rhyming couplets.

The lesson

1. Discuss with the class things that they do at school.
2. Read the example of the alphabet poem provided.
3. In their groups, the pupils are given letters of the alphabet to write their poem about school. Rhyming couplets must be used.
4. Each group reads out its poem. This is done in order from A to Z.
5. The pupils put their poems together. They can be rewritten neatly.
6. Display the class poem under the title, *'The A-Z of school'*. It should be displayed where others in the school can read it.
7. The pupils write their favourite rhyming couplets from the poem.

Answers

1. – 5. Teacher check

Additional activities

Pupils can:

1. As a class, write a list of events that have occurred throughout the year.
2. Write a class newspaper.
3. Contribute to the school's web page.

1 Read the poem below.

> *A is for the ABCs we go through every day,*
> *B is for the ball games, we're not allowed to play!*
> *C is for the chalk the teacher uses to write words,*
> *D is for the dance lessons, that make us look like nerds!*
> *E is for the extra work when we make a noise,*
> *F is for the fear we feel when Miss says, 'Come here boys!'*
> *G is for the 'Good' remark we do not often get,*
> *H is for the horror when our project's not done yet!*

2 Find a small group to work with. Your group will be given some letters of the alphabet. Use them to write an alphabet poem about your activities at school. Make them sound exciting and fun because they are!

As a group, write your letters and your poem. Use rhyming couplets!

_____

_____

_____

_____

_____

_____

_____

_____

3 Read your poems aloud together, group by group, starting with A.

4 Put your poems together and display them for the rest of the school to see. Use the title: **'The A – Z of school'**.

5 Write your favourite rhyming couplets from the whole poem.

• _____

_____

• _____

_____

Bad day

Objective
Discuss issues in poems that directly affect his/her life

Activities covered
- Reading a poem
- Answering questions
- Completing a sentence
- Writing a haiku poem
- Discussing a poem
- Taking part in a class discussion

Background information
This lesson concentrates on what causes people to have a bad day. Discussion should focus on real and everyday problems the pupils may have. The teacher and class should be sensitive to the feelings of others. Issues that can be discussed may include: friends, family, school, bullies, sport and interests. The pupils should decide what affects their lives and, therefore, the ideas should come from them. At the end of the lesson, the pupils write a haiku. The format of a haiku can be very complicated but here it has been simplified to 5/7/5 syllables and a title. Although haikus are usually about nature, the pupils will be writing about having a bad day. Full sentences and rhyming are not required in writing a haiku.

Before the lesson
Prepare examples of other websites/telephone numbers for advice centres for the pupils.

The pupils can write down 10 things that affect their lives, in a good or bad way. This can be done prior to this lesson, for homework.

The lesson
1. Read the poem **'Don't say it!'** as a class.
2. Discuss the poem. The pupils can comment on whether the poet is right to complain.
3. The pupils write about what happened in the poem and what might make the poet feel better.
4. The pupils complete the sentence given in Question 5.
5. The pupils write a haiku about having a bad day. The format could be discussed first.
6. The pupils discuss their poem with the class. (Because the poem could be personal, the pupils do not have to share their poems with the class.)
7. Hold a class discussion about what affects the pupils' day.

Answers
1. Teacher check
2. fly in pie, cat brings rat, met a shark, power is down, no dinner, row with friend
3. Answers will vary but might include:
   He/She would feel better if the power came back on and his/her friend rang to make amends.
4. – 7. Teacher check

Additional activities
Pupils can:
1. Write about the perfect day. (They could listen to the song 'Perfect day' [Hoku Lyrics] as they are writing!)
2. Become familiar with websites/advice centres they could contact if they wished to contact a support person anonymously; e.g. *www.childline.org.uk* or *www.kidsgethelp.org.uk* Emphasise that they must only do this with reputable websites!
3. Use improvisational drama to highlight common problems.
4. Read problem pages from pupils' magazines/websites.

Recommended reading

It wasn't me by Steve Turner
A way with words by Wes Magee
It is a puzzle by Allan Ahlberg
New baby by Jackie Kay
Who started it? by Michael Rosen
Nightmare by Steve Turner

There are many things that can affect the kind of day we are having. I hope you are having a good one today!

1 Read the poem below.
Have you ever had a day like this?

Don't say it!

Just when you say,
'This is a great day!'
Something is sure to go wrong.

A fly in your pie,
Brings you down from your high,
Your happiness didn't last long.

Cat brings in a rat,
So proud of the fact,
As he purrs while licking his paws.

A swim in the sea,
And you have to break free,
From a shark who has snappy jaws.

The power's gone down,
All over town,
Your microwave meal helps a ton.

A row with a friend,
Will this day ever end?
Wake me up when this one is done!

2 Name three bad things that happened to this person.

_____

_____

_____

3 What might make him/her feel better?

_____

_____

4 What do you think is the worst thing that happened? Why?

_____

_____

_____

5 Complete the sentence. | A problem shared is a problem halved. |

I have a bad day when _____

_____

6 Write a HAIKU poem about a bad day.
Follow the example.

| In a haiku, you do not need full sentences or rhyme. |

Long minutes	Title	_____
seconds tick over	5 syllables	_____
so slow, time seems to stand still	7 syllables	_____
all day at this school	5 syllables	_____

7 Read your poem to the class if you wish.

Objective

Discuss different possible solutions to problems

Activities covered

- Answering questions
- Reading a poem
- Predicting an outcome
- Writing about problems
- Discussing problems and possible solutions

Background information

Pupils need the opportunity to talk freely about common problems and come up with possible solutions. The pupils should feel confident to discuss things in class without being ridiculed. It is the teacher's role to keep the right atmosphere. This lesson should be primarily discussion.

Recommended reading

It is a puzzle by Allan Ahlberg

Names by Jackie Kay

Looking for Dad by Brian Patten

I'm the youngest in our house by Michael Rosen

Having my ears boxed by Roger McGough

Playing tennis with Justin by David Harmer

Best friends by Adrian Henri

Me by Kit Wright

Excuses, excuses by Catharine Boddy

A way with words by Wes Magee

Before the lesson

Prepare a list of common problems that may affect this age group to discuss with the class.

The lesson

1. As a class, discuss common problems other pupils of the same age group may have. Possible solutions to these problems can also be explored.
2. The pupils write what makes a good friend and what does not. They should be writing full sentences.
3. Read the poem **'An apple a day'** and discuss it as a class. More difficult words can be explained by the teacher, such as 'deceptive', 'feeble', 'fateful'.
4. The pupils predict what they think may have happened to the poet to complete Question 4.
5. The pupils write possible problems they may have with friends.
6. As a class, discuss how these problems could be solved/alleviated.

Answers

1. Answers will vary, but may include:
   loyal, kind, friendly, interested, understanding, supportive, fun to be with etc.
2. Answers will vary, but may include:
   angry, jealous, untrustworthy, secretive, unkind, selfish etc.
3. – 4. Teacher check
5. Answers will vary, but may include:
   keep a secret, get jealous about other friends you have, talk about you behind your back, lose interest in you etc.
6. Teacher check

Additional activities

Pupils can:

1. Write a problem and a solution to the problem. These can be put together to form a 'Problem page'.
2. Read problem pages from magazines. (These need to be pupil-oriented magazines and the teacher should check content.)
3. Look at advice websites.
4. Become familiar with phone numbers to call if they have a problem.
5. Work on the same set of problems in groups. The solutions can then be discussed as a class.

Homework suggestion

The pupils can write down a problem anonymously; these can be handed to the teacher to discuss at the start of the lesson.

Friends are important, but sometimes friendships can go wrong.

1 What do you think makes a good friend?

Someone who is … _____

_____

2 What do you think makes a bad friend?

Someone who is … _____

_____

3 Read about this person's experience in the poem below.

An apple a day

A bad friend is like an apple,
Sweet to the taste at first,
But after a few mouthfuls,
You'll see it at its worst.

For at its deceptive, juicy core,
Lies a slimy worm in wait,
And once you've got your teeth sunk in,
It may just be too late.

You'll realise then the fruit is bad,
You'll feel feeble, pale and ill,
And many years after that fateful bite,
You'll feel the terror still.

> A friend in need is a friend indeed.

4 What do you think could have happened?

_____

_____

_____

_____

_____

_____

_____

5 What kind of problems could someone have with a friend?

_____

_____

_____

_____

_____

6 Discuss with the class how you could deal with these problems.

Objective

Read poem with a partner and answer questions about it

Activities covered

- Reading poem
- Reading a poem with a partner
- Answering questions
- Discussing dangerous situations
- Predicting an ending to a poem

Background information

This lesson focuses on dangerous situations. Discuss with the class what effects dangerous behaviour may have. The bulk of the lesson should be discussion about dangerous situations the pupils may find themselves in, and possible solutions to get out of these situations.

Before the lesson

Divide the class into pairs.

The lesson

1. Read the poem *'Good intentions'* as a class. The poem can then be read aloud, with half the class saying the lion's part and the other half saying the rabbit's part.

2. In pairs, the pupils read the poem, with each pupil reading a character.

3. The pupils answer questions about the dangers involved in the poem and predict an outcome.

4. The pupils discuss the poem and dangerous situations they may find themselves in. The pupils should think of possible dangers they may have to face. They should decide on solutions to avoid or mitigate these dangers. The pupils could predict outcomes for various dangerous situations.

Answers

1. – 6. Teacher check

Additional activities

Pupils can:

1. Look at causes and effects in other subjects.

2. Read stories and predict outcomes before the end of the story.

3. Read newspaper articles and look at the causes behind the events.

You will probably have several conversations with different people during the day.

1 As a class, read the conversation below.

Good intentions

Lion: Good day, Mr Rabbit, and how do you do?

Rabbit: Don't come any closer, I do not trust you.

Lion: Now, now, Mr R, there's no need to fear.

Rabbit: I'll scream blue murder if you come near!

Lion: Relax, I'm not hungry, in fact, I just ate.

Rabbit: I bet you wouldn't mind seeing **me** on your plate.

Lion: Hah! You're barely a starter, just a mere scrap!

Rabbit: Yes, well I'm off now before I get trapped.

Lion: Ah, that is a pity, I enjoy your company.

Rabbit: Goodbye, Mr Lion, please let me go free.

Lion: Hey, sure, Mr Bunny, but come visit my den,
I look forward to eating … I mean, meeting you again!

In hard times, lions have been known to eat melons and cucumbers!

2 Read aloud the conversation with a partner. Each choose a character to play.

3 Do you think this is a dangerous situation? Say why/why not.

_____

_____

4 What dangerous situation could you find yourself in?

_____

5 What would you do?

_____

6 What do you think might happen next to the rabbit and the lion?

_____

_____

Brotherly love

Objective

Explore reactions to poems through improvisational drama

Activities covered

- Reading a poem as a group
- Answering questions
- Acting out a poem in pairs
- Commenting on peer performances
- Discussing a poem as a class

Background information

Through acting, pupils can explore their feelings towards different ideas. Acting should be informal and fun as long as the pupils keep to the basic storyline. The pupils can also add their own ideas.

Before the lesson

Divide the class into groups, preferably with even numbers.

The lesson

1. In groups, the pupils read the poem *'Sibling revelry'* together. The teacher can explain more difficult words or terms such as 'sibling revelry', 'battle zone' and 'tentatively'.

2. The pupils answer Questions 2 – 4 on their copymaster. These can be done as a group.

3. In pairs, the pupils act out the poem for the group. They can practise it a few times before their performance. They can also add their own parts as long as they fit in with the storyline.

4. The pupils comment on each other's performances, keeping those comments positive and constructive.

5. The poem and performances are discussed as a class.

Answers

1. Teacher check
2. (a) false   (b) false   (c) true   (d) true   (e) false
3. – 6. Teacher check

Additional activities

Pupils can:

1. Act out scenes from other subjects such as history.
2. Act out sections of the class reader.

1 Read the poem below as a group.

> Blood is thicker than water.

Sibling Revelry
(You had to be there)

Mum and Dad went out one day,
My brother and I were alone.
Now, usually we fight like cat and dog,
It's a bit like a battle zone.

I was expecting him to fight with me,
Or scream at me, 'Get out!'
But he calmly looked at me and said,
'What's your book about?'

I tentatively looked at him,
And briefly told the story.
He said, 'Nah, that doesn't sound good,
It isn't very gory'.

The afternoon just drifted by,
We watched stuff on TV.
We even made popcorn and milkshakes,
Together, just him and me.

Mum would be so proud,
To see us get on so well.
I couldn't believe this change about,
And I couldn't wait to tell.

Then Mum and Dad got home.
I looked at my brother with love,
He said, 'What the heck are you looking at –
shut up or I'll give you a shove!'

2 Write **TRUE** or **FALSE** for the following statements.

(a) This brother and sister usually get on well.

_____

(b) They fought when their parents left.

_____

(c) The sister was pleased they were getting along.

_____

(d) The brother and sister were doing things together.

_____

(e) Their mum was proud of them that day.

_____

3 What do you think the sister may have said when their parents arrived?

_____

_____

4 What advice would you give this brother and sister?

_____

_____

_____

5 As a group, take turns to act out the poem, two at a time.

6 Comment on each other's performances.

Objective

Extend participation in listening activities

Activities covered

- Listening to teacher
- Answering questions
- Saying/Reading a joke to a partner
- Retelling jokes
- Giving and retelling descriptions

Background information

Give the pupils the opportunity for silent reading sessions during class time. Pupils should also listen to others reading and support the weaker readers. Listening skills should be tested frequently.

Before the lesson

Have the poem *'To bath or not to bath?'* ready to read to the class (see below).

Divide the class into pairs.

Pupils can bring their own joke for Question 4.

The lesson

1. Read the poem *'To bath or not to bath?'* to the class slowly and clearly. The poem is not discussed.
2. The pupils answer Question 2.
3. The poem is re-read. The pupils mark their answers and write down their score to complete Question 3.
4. In pairs, the pupils choose one of the two jokes and read it to their partner. Alternatively, they can tell their own joke.
5. The partner retells the joke.
6. Still in pairs, partners describe their bathrooms; the other must repeat the description.

Answers

1. Teacher check
2. (a) his mother
   (b) sensitive
   (c) bubble bath
   (d) yes
   (e) spotty skin
   (f) tub/something sticky
   (g) hairspray
   (h) true
   (i) put them in a line, added them all to the bath
   (j) He thought it was a waste of time./He did not enjoy it.
3. – 5. Teacher check

To bath or not to bath?

I was sent up to the bathroom,
To get really clean, I s'pose.
Mum said I must be shining,
From my head down to my toes.

I stared at all the products,
That I was meant to use.
I knew I should use most of them,
Or Mum would blow a fuse.

There was soap for sensitive skin,
Conditioner and shampoo,
Some funny-smelling bubble bath,
And body lotion too.

There was stuff to clean your face with,
And cream to clear up spots,
Perfume and deodorant,
Detangle, to take out knots.

A tub of something sticky,
That would make me young again.
Would it make me a baby,
Because I was only ten?

Toothpaste, mouthwash, tea-tree oil,
Face masks and hairspray,
Foaming gel and aftershave,
This would take all day!

I didn't have time for all of this,
So I put the stuff in a line,
And added some of each to the bath,
Now I smell just fine!

Additional activities

Pupils can:

1. Participate in designated silent reading periods in the classroom.
2. Tell each other stories in groups. The group can then ask questions about the story.
3. Listen to others giving a talk.

Recommended reading

Washing by Steve Turner

Your listening skills are about to be tested!

1 Listen carefully while the teacher reads.

2 Answer these questions.

(a)   Who told the boy he had to have a bath?   _____

(b)   What skin type was the soap for?   _____

(c)   Which product had a funny smell?   _____

(d)   Was there mouthwash in the bathroom?   _____

(e)   What was the cream for?   _____

(f)   What product promised to make you younger?   _____

(g)   Name a spray that was mentioned.   _____

(h)   True or false? There was shampoo and conditioner. _____

(i)   What did the boy do with all the products?

_____

(j)   How did the boy feel about bathing?

_____

3 How well did you listen? Write your score: /₁₀

4 Find a partner to work with. Choose or think of one joke each to say or read to each other. Your partner must tell you the joke back!

What kind of dog likes to take bubble baths?

Shampoodles!

What animal do you look like when you get into the bath?

A little bear!

5 Still in pairs, describe your bathroom to your partner. He/She must describe it back to you!

Point of view

Objective

Explore other points of view and perspectives through reading

Activities covered

- Reading a poem
- Answering questions
- Thinking of other points of view

Background information

Through reading, pupils can explore different perspectives and viewpoints. Seeing things from another's point of view will teach them to be more tolerant and accepting. Although this lesson does involve reading the poem, it is also about seeing things from a different perspective.

Before the lesson

Provide other poems that convey the poet's point of view.

The lesson

1. Discuss with the class scenarios that give different perspectives/points of view. For example, telling a friend you are too busy to come over and play, what might the friend be thinking? etc.
2. Read the poem *'Tough enough'* as a class and discuss it. More difficult words can be explained, such as 'coo', 'accomplished', 'affection', 'smother', 'harass', 'reign'.
3. To answer Question 2, the pupils write whether the owner would be surprised by the cat's point of view.
4. The pupils then write the cat's feelings in their own words.
5. The pupils write what their pet might say. (If a pupil doesn't have a pet, he/she could write about someone else's pet.)
6. The pupils write two thought bubbles to complete Question 5. They should be writing it from the mum/teacher's point of view, not their own.
7. To answer Question 6, the pupils write what three different people might think if they saw a pot of red paint.

Answers

1. – 4. Teacher check
5. Examples Mum might be thinking: 'That could be dangerous'.
   Teacher might be thinking: 'Did he even try to do his homework?'
6. Teacher check

Additional activities

Pupils can:

1. Read about other pupils' interests and hobbies.
2. Read about the lives of others; e.g. authors like Roald Dahl or Dr Seuss, musical band members, pop stars, actors, famous explorers.
3. Read and discuss feats found in the *Guinness book of world records*.
4. Explore the feelings of others through reading poetry.
5. Look at different situations from the points of view of all those involved; e.g. in a restaurant – what might the diners be thinking?/what might the manager be thinking?/what might the waiters be thinking?/what might the chef be thinking?
6. Go on a fact-finding mission with topics given by the teacher.

Recommended reading

Is everyone in bed now? by Steve Turner

Walkies by Mike Johnson

A diner apologises by Stewart Henderson

The wolf's excuse by Yvonne Coppard

Who said what? by Gervase Phinn

Cat message by Roger Stevens

It is good sometimes to think of somebody else's point of view.

1 Read the poem below.

Tough enough

Why do you speak in that tone of voice?
I'm not a child, you know.
I'm seven times two is what I am,
And I'm free to come and go.

Why do you brag to all your friends,
About all the things I've done?
I've accomplished more than you'll ever know,
Long distances I've run.

I'll decide when I need affection,
Don't smother and harass me,
Don't follow me around the place,
Please, just leave me be.

You needn't worry about my safety,
I'm a brave and fearless brat,
I reign over this neighbourhood,
After all, I am a cat.

2 Do you think the owner would be surprised about how the cat feels?

_____

3 Write in your own words what this cat is trying to say to its owner.

4 What might your pet say to you if he/she could talk?

5 What do you think the other person's point of view would be if you said:

Mum, I'm just going to swim in the lake.

Mum

Miss, the homework was too hard so I didn't bother.

Teacher

6 What might each of these people think if they saw a tin of red paint?

(a) doctor

_____

_____

(b) decorator

_____

_____

(c) pupil

_____

_____

Surf the web

Objective

Continue to use information technology to increase motivation to read and to enhance reading development

Activities covered

- Looking at a website
- Answering questions
- Using a search engine
- Writing a lune

Background information

The pupils need to have the opportunity to look at sites that interest them, and become accustomed to searching on the web. The teacher will obviously have to check suitability of sites. Supervision while pupils are on the Internet is a high priority.

Lune:

American haiku which can be either syllable or word counting:

Words	Syllables
1st line: 3 words	1st line: 5 syllables
2nd line: 5 words	2nd line: 3 syllables
3rd line: 3 words	3rd line: 5 syllables

Before the lesson

Each pupil will need sufficient time on the Internet looking at the given websites. This lesson could be taken over a few weeks, with each pupil having time on the Internet while others in the class are engaged on a different task.

Check that the websites given in Question 1 are still current. If not, some alternatives will need to be found and listed.

The lesson

1. The pupils choose a website from the list given in Question 1.
2. Read the questions on the copymaster with the class to make sure all pupils understand the terms used; e.g. links to other sites.
3. The pupils answer questions about the website.
4. The pupils use a search engine to find out what a 'lune poem' is.
5. The pupils write a lune. The teacher can help the pupils with the format and the class could write one together, deciding whether they want to count syllables or words.
6. All questions can be discussed as a class, and the class can decide which was the best website.

Answers

1. – 7. Teacher check

Additional activities

Pupils can:

1. Look at websites about areas of interest; e.g. pop groups, TV programmes, games, sport. (The teacher will need to keep a check on the content.)
2. Keep a list of good websites in the classroom, and continually add to it.
3. Use search engines to find information about topics the pupils are studying in other subjects.

Website

(lune)

<http://ettcweb.lr.k12.nj.us/forms/lune.htm>

To 'surf the web' means to look up information on the Internet. Always check with an adult before 'surfing'!

1 Look at one of these websites.

www.poetry4kids.com

www.gigglepoetry.com

www.fizzyfunnyfuzzy.com

2 Circle the one you chose.

3 Name one poem you enjoyed reading on the website. Give the poet's name.

_____

_____

4 Write a verse from the poem.

_____

_____

_____

_____

_____

5 Tick the features the website had.

(a) **pictures** ☐   (b) **music** ☐   (c) **advertising** ☐   (d) **links to other sites** ☐

6 Use a search engine to find out how to write a LUNE. (American haiku).

7 Write your own lune about the INTERNET.

_____

_____

_____

www stands for World Wide Web

Poetry skills   **95**

Book talk

Objective

Know the structure and terminology of books

Activities covered

- Looking at a poetry book as a group
- Answering questions
- Labelling a picture of book
- Reading poems

Background information

Teachers should occasionally refer to book terminology so that pupils become familiar with the vocabulary. It is not necessary for the pupils to know all terms by heart, but they should be familiar with them.

Before the lesson

Divide the class into groups.

Each group will need a poetry book. These poetry books should be interesting and enticing! The book can be written by a single poet or be an anthology of poetry.

The lesson

1. Discuss the terminology associated with books, using examples to illustrate the meanings.
2. Provide each group with a poetry book. Each group passes the book around for all members to look at.
3. In their groups, the pupils answer Questions 2 and 3. Full sentences are not required.
4. The pupils label the book illustration to complete Question 4.
5. Pupils take turns to read some of the poems in the book to each other.

Answers

1. – 5. Teacher check

Additional activities

Pupils can:

1. Visit the school/local library and take time to look through the books. Find the different parts of a book.
2. Display books in the classroom, using labels they have made to show the different parts of a book.
3. Each explain a 'book term' to the class. They only need to say a few words and perhaps use an example to show the class. Terms that could be used include: caption, illustration, author, index, title, spine, publisher, front cover, back cover, table of contents, chapter, dedication, copyright, ISBN number, bibliography or reviews.
4. Play a game where the teacher calls out a book term and the pupils have to find it on a book. The pupils could be in groups for this activity.

Recommended reading

Oh am I still here? by Jan Dean

Worst sellers by Lindsay MacRae

For word by Benjamin Zephaniah

Breakfast reading by Steve Turner

1 In a small group, look closely at a poetry book. Pass it around for everyone to see.

2 As a group, answer these questions.

(a) What is the title of the book?_____

(b) Which company published the book? _____

(c) Who is the author of the book? _____

(d) Name something that is found on the back cover. _____

(e) When was it first published? _____

(f) Is it illustrated? _____

(g) Does the book have these? Tick them if 'yes'.

Table of contents.........☐

Index ....☐

Chapters ....☐

Introduction ....☐

Bibliography................☐

(h) Is the book dedicated to someone? If so, who? _____

(i) How many pages does the book have? _____

(j) What is written on the spine? _____

3 Write the title of one poem (and the poet) that can be found in the book.

_____

4 Draw different coloured lines from the words to label the correct parts of the book.

spine, front cover, illustration, author, title, pages, publisher, back cover

5 Read some of the poems in the book you have been looking at to each other.

Objective

Continue to develop a range of comprehension strategies to deal with reading material

Activities covered

- Reading an epitaph
- Answering questions
- Writing a two-line epitaph

Background information

It is not only important that pupils read, but that they understand what they are reading. There is a variety of ways to give pupils practice in comprehension, so exercises should not be restricted. Pupils need to become accustomed to reading a wide range of texts, including timetables, charts, graphs, captions, tables, diagrams, lists, forms etc.

Before the lesson

Prepare another example of reading material with a comprehension activity for the class to do together.

The lesson

1. Share the example of reading material (e.g. diagram with labels) with the class and have the pupils answer questions.

2. Explain what an epitaph is. The term 'conservationist' could also be explained as someone who is concerned with conserving or preserving the natural environment.

3. The pupils read the epitaph provided and answer Question 2. This can be done individually.

4. The pupils write a two-line poem for an epitaph, using a fictional character. The name of the fictional character should be on the first line. It is important that the pupils use a *fictional* character so that feelings are not hurt, and also so that they can choose a name for easy rhyming.

5. All answers can be discussed as a class.

Answers

1. Teacher check
2. (a) Rose
   (b) yes
   (c) 81
   (d) Teacher check (maybe Peter as this is the son's name)
   (e) kind, trustworthy, nature lover, loved outdoors, loving, gentle etc.
   (f) Yes, he enjoyed fishing/he was a conservationist.
   (g) Teacher check
   (h) Rest in Peace
3. Teacher check

Additional activity

Pupils can:

Read the following texts and answer comprehension questions: menus, recipes, lists, timetables, poetry, adverts, TV listings, film line-ups, instructions, road signs, messages, letters, articles, cartoon strips, tables of information, web pages, text messages, for sale columns, property sales, bills, captions, headlines, lyrics.

Homework suggestion

If there is a graveyard or cemetery nearby, the pupils can go to look at and read the tombstones.

Recommended reading

Graveyard by John Kitching

Epitaph for the last Martian by Paul Cookson

E-PET-APH by Andrew Fusek Peters

Nightmare Cemetery by Adrian Henri

An epitaph is the words written on a headstone.

1 Read the epitaph below.

1916 – 1997

Here lies John P Hall

He was dearly loved by all.

Beloved husband of Rose, loving father of Amanda and Peter,

True friend and trusted neighbour,

Fisherman and conservationist

'Love rules a kingdom without a sword'

RIP

2 Answer these questions:

(a) What was the name of this man's wife?

_____

(b) Did he have a son?

☐ Yes ☐ No

(c) What age was this man when he died?

_____

(d) What might the 'P' stand for in his name?

_____

(e) What kind of a man do you think he was?

_____

_____

_____

_____

(f) Do you think he liked nature? Say why.

_____

_____

_____

_____

(g) What does the quote mean?

_____

_____

_____

_____

(h) What does RIP stand for?

_____

_____

3 Write a two-line rhyming poem for an epitaph. Use a made-up name in the first line.

_____

_____

Baby talk

Objective

Use a knowledge of printing conventions as an aid to expression and comprehension

Activities covered

- Reading a poem
- Answering questions
- Writing a poem using printing conventions
- Reading sentences
- Rewriting a given sentence

Background information

There are many visual cues that can help to give more meaning and expression to what we read. Discuss the following with the class: punctuation marks, use of capital letters and italic and bold print. Pupils should be made aware of different printing conventions when reading and be using them in their own writing.

Before the lesson

Provide other examples of texts where different printing conventions have been used.

The lesson

1. Read the poem ***Huh?*** together as a class.
2. The pupils answer Question 2.
3. The pupils write their own poem, using the printing conventions already discussed. They only need to write a two-line poem as the rest can be 'baby talk' as in the example.
4. The pupils tick which sentence is stronger for Question 4. The class could discuss what makes the sentence stronger.
5. The pupils make a given sentence stronger to answer Question 5.

Answers

1. Teacher check
2. (a) two; Teacher check
   (b) one; Teacher check
   (c) There is an accent on this word, it needs to be said louder or emphasised.
   (d) beginning of a sentence, proper noun (name)
3. Teacher check
4. (b) is the stronger sentence
5. e.g. I ***wish*** we had school on Saturdays!

Additional activities

Pupils can:

1. Look for different printing conventions in a class reader.
2. Improve the meaning and expression of given sentences by adding capital letters, italics, bold, exclamation marks etc. Sentences can be compared to see how they differ in meaning.
3. Look for printing conventions in magazines, newspapers, comics etc.
4. Discuss how printing conventions can place a different emphasis on the meaning of the sentence; e.g. I ***want*** you to visit me./I want you to visit ***me***.

1 Read the poem below.

> ### Huh?
>
> *Goo ba ba ba*
> *Goo bi bee*
> *Goo bi bu ba*
> *Goo bo be*
>
> *Little brother, what **was** that?*
> *Please speak English when you chat!*

2 Answer the questions.

(a) How many question marks are in the poem? _____ Use one in a sentence.

_____

(b) How many exclamation marks are there? _____ Use one in a sentence.

_____

(c) Why is the word '**was**' in bold type? _____

_____

(d) Underline the capital letters. Why are they used? _____

_____

3 Write your own poem using baby talk. Your poem must have a question mark, a capital letter, an exclamation mark and a word in bold type.

> Read your poem to the class! Use expression!

4 Read these sentences. Tick which sentence is stronger.

(a) 'Jim, you will tidy your room this minute.' .... ☐

(b) 'Jim, you **will** tidy your room **this minute!**' .... ☐

5 Rewrite this sentence, making it stronger, as though you really mean it!

I wish we had school on Saturdays.

Objective

Write a poem using rhyme and rhythm

Activities covered

- Reading a poem
- Writing a poem
- Answering questions
- Assessing own work

Background information

By this age, pupils should be writing with more sophistication, and should be encouraged to improve their work, if necessary. It is important that pupils are encouraged in a positive manner and not continuously told they 'can do better!' Pupils should be using correct spelling and grammar in their written tasks, but should also be writing using their imagination and trying to make their writing unique. Written tasks should be varied and of interest to the pupils. Rhyming and rhythm are important in this lesson.

Before the lesson

Prepare other examples of love poems to read to the pupils.

The lesson

1. Read the poem **'No love'** as a class and discuss. Mention the format and rhyme scheme. Explain more difficult words such as 'landlord' and 'cobbler'.
2. The pupils write their own poem using the same format. They can use the ending in the example or make up their own. Explain to the pupils that rhyme and rhythm are important.
3. The pupils answer Question 3.
4. The pupils comment on their own poem to complete Question 4.

Answers

1. – 2. Teacher check
3. No, he wants to meet her.
4. Teacher check

Additional activities

Pupils can:

1. Look at websites that contain love poems. (Teachers *must* check content first.)
2. Write texts in a variety of genres; e.g. film reviews, timetables, itineraries, school mottoes, product descriptions, slogans, weather reports, letters, thank you notes, speeches, plays.

Recommended reading

Fall in love by Fred Sedgwick

Whispers of love by Janis Priestley

Love has an effect on our teacher by John Coldwell

Romance by Brian Moses

Cyber love by Mike Jubb

1 Read the poem below.

No love

I love you not, I'm afraid,
I don't love you at all,
If I were a ladder,
I'd give you a fall.

If I were a kitty cat,
I'd scratch and hiss at you,
If I were your personal chef,
I'd serve you lumpy stew.

If I were an ocean,
I'd send you a tidal wave,
And if I were your landlord,
I'd stick you in a cave.

If I were the TV,
I'd give you only news,
And if I were your cobbler,
I'd make you stinky shoes.

If I were your teacher,
You'd do hard sums every day,
If I were your road map,
I'd make sure you lost your way.

So now perhaps you realise,
How much I feel for you,
But if you're free on Friday,
Could you meet me at about two?

Do not direct this poem at anyone as it would hurt their feelings!

2 Write your own poem, using the same patterns of rhyme and rhythm. You may like to draft your poem on a separate sheet of paper first.

I love you not, I'm afraid,

I don't love you at all,

If I were a _____ ,

I'd _____ .

If I were a _____ ,

_____ ,

_____ ,

_____ .

If I were _____ ,

_____ ,

_____ ,

_____ .

_____ ,

_____ ,

_____ ,

_____ .

Rhyming and rhythm are important!

3 Do you think this poet really dislikes this person? Say why/why not. _____

_____

4 Read your poem to yourself. Write a comment about your completed poem.

_____

In your own words

Objective

Read a poem and write it as a story in his/her own words

Activities covered

- Reading a poem
- Discussing poem
- Writing poem as a story, using own words
- Answering questions

Background information

Explain to the pupils that they should never copy the words of others and use them as their own writing. It's actually against copyright law! They need to know that if they are quoting someone, they should use quotation marks.

Before the lesson

Prepare examples of how we write something in our own words.

The lesson

1. Read the poem *'Beefy breakfast'* as a class and discuss the sequence of the poem and any words or terms that may need clarifying; e.g. 'laden', 'Yorkshire puddings'.

2. The pupils write the poem as a story in their own words, using full sentences and writing in the first or second person.

3. The pupils read their story to themselves.

4. The pupils write what they think was packed for lunch.

Answers

1. – 3. Teacher check

Additional activities

Pupils can:

1. Put together all the stories with the original poem in a booklet to be left in the school library for others to read.

2. Read online stories and write them in their own words.

3. Write well-known fairytales in their own words, or rewrite them as a newspaper article.

4. Use their own words when doing projects in other subjects.

Homework suggestion

The pupils read a simple poem and write it in their own words, without any rhyme.

When doing any sort of writing activities, you should always use your own words. You would not like it if someone stole your words!

❶ Read the poem below.

Beefy breakfast

I woke up as usual this morning,
and stumbled down the stairs,
I went in to have my breakfast,
and sat on one of the chairs.

I thought perhaps I was seeing things,
perhaps I was not awake,
but no, there was a huge roast beef,
and veggies for goodness sake!

The table was laden with hot, cooked food,
no cereal or toast in sight,
but Yorkshire puddings and gravy,
this did not feel right!

I looked at Mum with confusion,
but she was singing a happy song,
while washing heaps of pots and pans,
like there was nothing wrong!

I dished up a big plate of 'dinner',
ate as much as I could munch,
I washed it down with trifle and cream—I
wonder what Mum packed for lunch!

Mum: Eat up your roast beef, it's full of iron!
Dave: No wonder it's so tough!

❷ Write the poem as a story using your own words and full sentences.

_____

_____

_____

_____

_____

_____

_____

_____

_____

_____

_____

_____

_____

_____

Read your story
to yourself!

❸ What do you think this mother packed in his lunch box?

_____

_____

_____

_____

Poetry skills

Main points only

Objective

Read a poem and summarise it

Activities covered

- Underlining main points
- Rewriting sentences
- Reading and summarising a poem
- Summarising a speech bubble

Background information

Pupils should be having some practice in summarising, such as summarising chapters in the class reader book, other poems, and text in other learning areas. Pupils should know that summarising means making something shorter by including only the most important facts. Provide the pupils with examples of summarising used in our everyday lives; e.g. telling someone about our day, relaying a telephone message.

Before the lesson

Prepare short examples of text that the class can summarise together.

The lesson

1. Complete some examples of summarising texts together as a class.
2. The pupils underline the most important points in a given sentence then rewrite the sentence.
3. Read the poem *'12 o'clock feeding'* as a class. The pupils can then underline what they consider to be the main points. The different types of food are not an important issue and should therefore not be included in this list. Harder words could be discussed, such as 'bustling', 'acquired', 'ceased', 'Sandman'.
4. The pupils summarise the poem by writing the main points only. These should still be full sentences. The pupils read their summary.
5. The pupils summarise the speech bubble to complete Question 5.

Answers

1. cat followed me, and I had to keep her forever.
2. The cat followed me home and I had to keep her forever.
3. main points – we tiptoed down stairs, we needed to eat, we sneaked to kitchen, mountain of food, quite tired, sleepiness, nibbled, no longer hungry
4. Answers will vary, but should be similar to the following:

   We went down the stairs and into the kitchen. We prepared a mountain of food as we were hungry. We got tired though and ate only a little. Our midnight feast was ruined by sleepiness.
5. Answers will vary, but should be similar to the following:

   'Your maths isn't finished so you will have to finish it during break.'

Additional activities

Pupils can:

1. Summarise various texts; e.g. work covered in other learning areas, such as learning work for a test.
2. Summarise a chapter in the class reader.
3. Summarise an advertisement by writing one sentence only.
4. Summarise pupils' song words. (Pupils can try to sing their new version!)
5. Summarise factual information by using tables/graphs/flow charts etc.

To summarise means to use only the most important information.

1 Underline what you think are the most important points in this sentence.

The beautiful, fluffy cat followed me all the way through the town, right to my cosy home and I had no choice really but to keep her and love her forever.

2 Rewrite the sentence by summarising it. It must still be a full sentence!

_____

_____

3 Underline the main points in the poem below.

> ## 12 o'clock feeding
> We tiptoed quietly down the wooden stairs,
> clutching our favourite teddy bears.
> Our tummies were rumbling, we needed to eat,
> we sneaked to the kitchen in slippered feet.
> We took out crisps and bread and jam,
> as well as cheese and honeyed ham.
> We found some nuts and a piece of cake,
> leftover chips and garlic steak.
> It wasn't enough, we needed more,
> we pulled out sausages from the freezer drawer.
> We fried them quickly in a pan,
> and dished out baked beans from a can.
> Then there we sat with our mountain of food,
> I wasn't sure now if we were quite in the mood.
> All of this bustling had made us quite tired,
> there was a sleepiness we'd all acquired.
> We nibbled a little, our appetites ceased.
> The Sandman had ruined our
> midnight feast.

> The Sandman is an elf in fairy stories who sprinkles sand in children's eyes to make them sleepy.

4 Summarise the main facts of the poem.

_____

_____

_____

_____

_____

_____

_____

_____

Reread your summary to make sure you have all the main points.

5 Summarise this speech bubble on the back of the worksheet.

> You have not finished your maths even though you have had about an hour to do it! What have you been doing all this time? Have you been chattering again? You will stay in at break and complete all of it, correctly!

Home sweet home

Teachers notes

Objective

Write about ideas encountered in other areas of the curriculum

Activities covered

- Writing about own home
- Discussing homes from around the world
- Writing a four-line poem
- Drawing and writing a poem in a shape

Background information

There are many opportunities for pupils to do written tasks in other areas of the curriculum, and the writing should be given as much importance as it is in English lessons. When writing for other subjects, written tasks should not be confined to answering questions, but should be varied and interesting.

Before the lesson

The pupils will need to have completed some research on a type of home. Teachers could allocate each pupil a type of home or allow the pupils to choose themselves.

The lesson

1. The pupils write a few sentences about their own home.
2. Hold a class discussion about different homes around the world. The pupils will have done some research on a particular type of home and they can share this information with the class. It is not necessary that the pupils research homes in different countries. They could research homes in their locality so that there is a variety of homes being discussed.
3. The list of different homes chosen by the pupils is discussed.
4. The pupils write a four-line poem about the home they researched. Rhyming is not necessary but would be preferable.
5. The pupils draw the home based on their earlier research and write their four-line poem in the shape.
6. All poems can be rewritten on a separate sheet of paper or card and then displayed in the classroom.

Answers

1. – 4. Teacher check

Additional activities

Pupils can:

1. Write stories, dialogues, short plays, newspaper articles, time lines, speeches, letters, cartoon strips, poetry, captions, flow charts, character sketches and reviews for history, geography or science.
2. Write story sums during maths.
3. Write experiments and draw flow charts, food chains and diagrams with labels, for science.

People around the world live in many different types of homes.

1 Describe your home.

_____

_____

_____

2 Have you heard of these?

> tepee, apartment, bungalow, detached house, semi-detached house, terraced house, hut, castle, log cabin, chalet, caravan, mobile home, tent, cottage, cabin, igloo, hotel, Bedouin tent, stilt house, houseboat

Choose one type of home from the list or one of your own. Write a four-line poem about the home, where it is and who it belongs to.

> Use rhyming words if you can!

> Some African people use cow dung when building their huts.

Title: _____

_____

_____

_____

_____

3 Draft work: Draw the home and write your four-line poem in the shape of it.

4 Redo your drawing and poem neatly on a separate sheet of paper or card and display it.

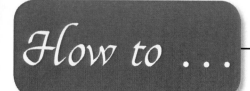

Objective
Write down directions on how to perform a particular process

Activities covered
- Reading a poem
- Writing a poem
- Improving on a poem

Background information
The pupils will need practice in writing directions or instructions. This lesson is a fun way to introduce writing instructions. From here, they can go on to writing more serious directions and instructions. The pupils should write the poem by starting each new idea on a new line, and by using full sentences for each idea. The pupils should write the poem in chronological order, starting with annoying or pleasing the teacher in the morning and ending with the close of the school day. Placing ideas in chronological order will give pupils a structure to use. Rhyming is not necessary.

Before the lesson
Prepare examples of processes to discuss briefly with the pupils.

The lesson
1. Read the poem *'How to annoy the teacher'*. Discuss why it would not be advisable to do the things in the poem; e.g. rocking on your chair is dangerous.
2. Explain the task to the pupils, discussing the chronological order in which they should write their own poem, as well as starting each new idea on a new line and using full sentences. Brief notes could be written on the board to remind the pupils.
3. The pupils write their own poems, in chronological order, if possible, as explained in 'Background information'.
4. The pupils read their poems to themselves and improve them if they can.
5. The finished poems can be put together as a booklet: 'How to annoy/please the teacher'. This should be left in the school library or somewhere that other pupils in the school have access to.

Answers
1. – 3. Teacher check

Additional activities
Pupils can:
1. Write directions on how to get to the school from a given point, how to get ready for school, how to do a school project, how to keep healthy etc.
2. Perform simple demonstrations.
3. Follow and write recipes.
4. Look at websites that show processes; e.g. (making chocolate) <www.fieldmuseum.org/chocolate/making.html>
5. Write babysitting instructions for themselves!
6. Write poems in a particular format.
7. Write about and/or demonstrate simple everyday tasks such as setting a table, feeding the cat, catching a bus, calling the emergency services, simple first aid procedures, playing a chord on the guitar, making tea, making a slice of toast, brushing teeth, making a bed, folding a shirt, doing a handstand, kicking a ball, drawing a dog etc.

Homework suggestion
Give the pupils a simple task as above, and have them prepare a demonstration to do the following day in class. The pupils should write their brief notes for their demonstration in point form.

Recommended reading
(Instructions)

How to make a mummy by Mike Jubb

How to scare your gran (but not mine) by Rita Ray

How to look after a teacher by Judith Nicholls

Instructions for giants by John Rice

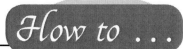

Do you know how to annoy the teacher? I hope you don't!

1 Read the poem below.

> Write your ideas in chronological order; that is, start with the morning and go through the day until home time.

How to annoy the teacher

Come to school late, without an excuse,
half-way through maths, open your juice.

Leave out the full stops in your
English essay,
ask for free time to go outside and play.

When you have a break, drop your
rubbish on the floor,
and when you come back, try slamming
the door.

Start rocking on your chair, as if
it's a boat,
put on your cap and leave on your coat.

During history time, let out a big yawn,
say you couldn't care less when your
country was born.

Chew away loudly on a blob of
bubble gum,
say science is boring, and
geography's dumb.

Talk all the time, get out of your seat,
start humming some tunes,
and put up your feet.

These things will all get the
teacher's attention,
but please don't blame me if you get
lifelong detention.

> Do not try these out!

> When is an English teacher like a judge?
> When he/she hands out long sentences!

2 Now write your own poem about ways to please or annoy the teacher! You may like to draft your poem on a separate sheet of paper first.

How to _____ the teacher.

_____

_____

_____

_____

_____

_____

_____

_____

_____

_____

_____

_____

_____

_____

_____

3 Read your poem to yourself. Improve it if you can.

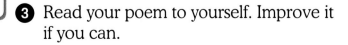

Add details

Objective

Write a sentence and elaborate on it by adding one or more ideas to it

Activities covered

- Reading example
- Discussing question words
- Matching questions and answers
- Adding to a sentence using rhyming couplets
- Reading a poem to self and class

Background information

Pupils can learn to make their writing more interesting by adding details. This can be introduced with pupils adding just adjectives to a noun. Pupils can use the **5 'W's** to help them to add details. (**When? Where? Why? Who? What?**)

Before the lesson

Pupils will need to be familiar with rhyming couplets.

The lesson

1. Pupils read the example of a rhyming couplet on the copymaster.
2. The teacher discusses with the class the question words, and how we can use questions to make our writing more interesting by adding details. Some examples can be done together as a class.
3. Pupils match up question words with the answers in the extended example.
4. Pupils add to the given rhyming couplets, using the question words to help them add more details. Pupils should be writing rhyming couplets.
5. Pupils read their poems to themselves and then to the class.

Answers

1. Teacher check
2. When?, How?, Where?, Why?
3. – 4. Teacher check

Additional activities

Pupils can:

1. Make a class story by each adding a detail to one sentence.
2. Add details to a simple sentence given to them by the teacher, by asking questions. The result will probably be more than one sentence.

We can make our sentences more interesting just by adding details!

1 Look at this example:

Sentence: *I just thought I'd let you know, I really have to go.*

This sentence does not give many details! We can ask questions and add more information. Remember questions start with Why? Who? When? How? Where? etc.

2 Match the question word with words or line answers in the poem.

I just thought I'd let you know, *I really have to go.*	• Why?
I need to go about 'now', *I'll find a lift somehow.*	• When?
	• Where?
I'm heading home early, Miss Jelly, *To relax and watch the telly.*	• How?

3 Add details to this sentence. Try to use rhyming couplets as in the example. Use the questions words to help you add more details.

> *I'm sorry I just can't stay,*
> *No matter what you say.*

Why? _____

_____

Where? _____

_____

When? _____

_____

How? _____

_____

4 Read your poem to yourself and then to the class.

Use the same questions when you are writing stories.

Check it again!

Objective

Expand and clarify his/her thoughts on a particular idea or topic through drafting and redrafting

Activities covered

- Reading a poem
- Underlining excuses
- Writing ideas – keywords
- Writing a poem using rhyming couplets
- Checking and redrafting a poem
- Rewriting and displaying a poem
- Holding a class vote

Background information

Pupils should be getting into the habit of drafting and redrafting their written work. The teacher needs to go through the process required to redraft a piece of work; e.g. making a plan, writing keywords, doing the task in draft form, checking spelling, punctuation and grammar, Can I improve on it?, Is there a better way of saying something? Is there something I could add to make the meaning clearer? A checklist can be left displayed in the classroom for the pupils to refer to. When checking their work, pupils should not hesitate to change their thoughts and ideas if they come up with better ones.

Recommended reading
(absent)

Tarzan misses school by John C Desmond

Excuses, excuses by Catharine Boddy

Letter from a super villain's mum
by Paul Cookson

Before the lesson

The pupils will need to understand the concept of drafting and redrafting a piece of work.

Pupils will need to know how to write a rhyming couplet.

The lesson

1. Read the poem *'Cured'* as a class and discuss. More difficult words can be explained, such as 'decorating', 'queasy', 'wreck' and 'ailments'.

2. The pupils underline the excuses in the poem.

3. The pupils think of five reasons why they cannot go to school. They must be given time to just think about the topic first. They can then write their ideas using keywords.

4. The pupils write a poem, giving excuses why they cannot go to school. The excuses can be as outrageous or farfetched as they like! Pupils should use rhyming couplets if possible.

5. The pupils check through their work carefully and try to improve it. Then check it again, referring to the checklist.

6. The pupils rewrite the poems neatly and display them in the classroom. They must be given the opportunity to read the work of others.

7. The class votes for the best excuse and the pupils write it down to answer Question 8.

Answers

1. Teacher check
2. Excuses – stomach ache, sore head, chest pain, watery eyes, runny nose, faint, queasy, cramps
3. Teacher check
4. Example:

    My toes are quite itchy, my elbow is sore.

    My nose, it is running, all over the floor

5. – 8. Teacher check

Additional activities

Pupils can:

1. Devise a list of questions to ask themselves, to be satisfied that the written work they have produced is the best they can do.

2. Redraft stories, poems, letters, paragraphs and other text types in other subjects.

Homework suggestion

The pupils can complete the redrafting process for homework if the exercise requires further time.

Always check your work carefully. Make sure it is the very best you can do!

1 Read the poem below.

Cured

'Oh, Mummy, I have a bad stomach ache,
I think it's that lumpy porridge you make.
Oh, Mummy, I have a terribly sore head,
I need a new pillow and a much softer bed.
Oh, Mummy, I have a horrid chest pain,
From walking home in the pouring rain.
Oh, Mummy, I have such watery eyes,
I think it's from your onion pies.
Oh, Mummy, I have a terribly runny nose,
I'm sure it's those flowers our neighbour grows.
Oh, Mummy, I feel a little faint,
I think it's your decorating with all that paint.
Oh, Mummy, I believe that I am queasy,
To stand up straight just isn't easy.
Oh, Mummy, I've cramps from my toes to my neck,
And back down again, why I feel a wreck!
Oh, Mummy, I don't think I'm up for
school,
With all these ailments, it would be just
cruel.'

'Oh, Molly, what a pity,
To be sick on a Saturday!'
'It's the weekend??? Ah well then,
I guess I feel OK.'

2 Underline the excuses in the poem.

3 Using keywords, write down five reasons why you cannot go to school.

_____

_____

_____

_____

_____

4 Write your ideas as rhyming couplets.

I cannot go to school because ...

_____

_____

_____

_____

_____

_____

_____

_____

_____

5 Check your work and try to improve it.

6 Check it again! Fix all mistakes. Make sure it is the best you can do! Give yourself a score out of 5.

/5

7 Rewrite and display your poem. Read your classmates' excuses!

8 Vote for the best class excuse. Write it on the back of this sheet.

You should only miss school if you have a valid reason!

Objective

Describe characters in a poem

Activities covered

- Naming and describing favourite characters
- Reading a poem
- Choosing and describing characters
- Answering questions

Background information

This lesson essentially revolves around discussion and getting the pupils to talk about their favourite characters in films, TV programmes, books, cartoons, comics etc. Pupils should be able to state *why* a particular character is one of their favourites.

Before the lesson

Examples of TV and film characters could be prepared.

The lesson

1. The pupils write a sentence about three of their favourite characters.
2. Read the poem *'Disguised'* as a class.
3. The pupils choose six characters from the poem and write a sentence about what each may have looked like.
4. The pupils write who they think would have looked the best/worst in the parade described in the poem.
5. The pupils write how they would dress up for a fancy dress party or parade.
6. All questions can be discussed as a class.

Answers

1. – 6. Teacher check

Additional activities

Pupils can:

1. Discuss favourite moments; e.g. from a school event, a birthday, Christmas.
2. Discuss and write about favourite characters in well-known fairytales.
3. Discuss favourite characters in a class reader.
4. Discuss and write about favourite scenes in a film/computer game.

Homework suggestion

The pupils write a description of a favourite character which they read to the class the following day. The class must guess who the character is.

Recommended reading

Colin by Allan Ahlberg

The evil Doctor Mucus Spleen by Paul Cookson

Mr Kartoffel by James Reeves

Our dad is a teacher by Mike Jubb

Gentle, sweet and deadly by Clive Webster

Sir's a secret agent by Tony Langham

My dad the headmaster by Paul Cookson

Our new headmaster by Ian Souter

Our teacher has us worried
by Barry Buckingham

Our head teacher by Brian Moses

Mr Fledermaus by Paul Bright

My step dad is an alien by Roger Stevens

The secret of a super villain by Andrew Collett

We all have favourite characters – in books, films, on TV or in cartoons.

1 List a favourite character from each of the following.

(a)   a book you have read _____

(b)   a TV programme _____

(c)   a film _____

2 Read the poem below.

Disguised

They paraded down the crowded street,
Marching to the pipe band beat.
The fancy dress was in full swing,
You wouldn't want to miss a thing.
Why, there was Shrek™, the princess too,
And Captain Hook with all his crew.
There was a monkey and bold, little Bart,
The weather man holding his cloudy chart.
I saw couch potatoes and funny clowns,
Strict schoolteachers wearing frowns.
An angel, a pop star, a cow and a cat,
A guard in uniform with a flashing hat.
Now I s'pose you are wondering, what was I?
Well, I was 'me' – an extraordinary guy.

3 Choose six characters from the poem and write a full sentence to describe them; e.g. 'The cat was fluffy and had huge claws'.

- _____
_____
- _____
_____
- _____
_____
- _____
_____
- _____
_____
- _____
_____

4 Who might have looked the best? _____

5 Who might have looked the worst? _____

_____

6 What would you wear to a fancy dress party or parade? Think of something original! Describe it.

_____

_____

Another time

Objective

Discuss reactions to poems

Activities covered

- Reading a poem as a group
- Answering questions
- Discussing a poem
- Writing an extra verse for a poem

Background information

Pupils need to express their thoughts honestly as long as they can show reasons for their thinking. In discussing reactions to poems, pupils need to talk about the poem at length and look at all points of view. There should be much discussion in this lesson.

Before the lesson

Prepare examples of old items to discuss with the pupils.

Divide the class into groups.

The lesson

1. Read the poem *'Another time'* as a class.
2. Discuss times long ago with the class. Work out with the pupils approximately when this grandfather was born. Show examples and pictures of items from his time, and discuss the things he would not have had.
3. The pupils read the poem with their groups and answer Questions 2 and 3.
4. The pupils discuss the poem and tell each other whether they liked it or not and why. The pupils could try to write a verse of their own if there is time.

Answers

1. – 5. Teacher check

Additional activities

Pupils can:

1. Read and discuss serious poetry.
2. Discuss poems written by the pupils as a class.
3. Read a poem and write a review.
4. Read a poem and write a letter to the poet.

Homework suggestion

The pupils read the poem to a family member and then discuss with an older family member what things he/she had when young.

Websites

<http://42explore.com/poetry.htm>

<www.gigglepoetry.com>

<www.poetry4kids.com/links.html>

1 Read the poem below with a small group.

2 In your groups, answer these questions.

Another time

I dreamed that my great, great, great grandad,
was sitting on my bed,
He died so many moons ago,
'Do not be afraid', he said.

'What's that box with people in it?
And why are they so small?'
'That's actually a television,
and they're not inside at all!'

'What is that hanging around your neck?
Is it a type of jewellery?'
'This is an MP3 player,
it holds loads of songs – for me.'

'What is that frightful, awful noise?
Oh no, is this country at war?'
'No, that is Mum using the hoover,
to clean the carpet and floor.'

'Oh, look at that poor girl in the box,
she's running and getting nowhere!'
'That's a treadmill in a gym,
and you pay to go in there.'

'Life seems very complicated,
though I think I'll be back soon,
Just to make sure you're all OK,
next you'll be on the moon!'

(a) How do you think the grandfather might have felt?

_____

(b) How would you feel if this happened to you?

_____

(c) List ten other items this grandfather would not have seen before.

_____
_____
_____
_____
_____
_____
_____
_____
_____
_____

3 How would you describe these things to the grandfather?

(a) a CD player: _____

(b) a mobile phone: _____

(c) a motorcar: _____

(d) a toaster: _____

(e) a PlayStation®: _____

4 Discuss the poem with your group and say whether or not you enjoyed the poem. Give reasons for your answer.

5 Try to write a verse of your own on a separate sheet of paper.

Imagine

Objective

Create and sustain imaginary contexts through improvisational drama

Activities covered

- Reading a poem as a group
- Brainstorming ideas for a dramatic scene
- Acting out a dramatic scene
- Assessing performance of a dramatic scene
- Creating a new ending for a familiar rhyme

Background information

For this type of lesson, discussion needs to play a big part. Pupils need to be discussing the topic at length, which they can then dramatise. Ideally, the pupils could practise their dramas outside where they have more room and freedom.

Before the lesson

Divide the class into groups.

The lesson

1. The pupils read the poem *'Pitter-patter'* in groups
2. Each group imagines a situation someplace outdoors where it is teeming with rain.
3. The pupils discuss the situation and write down keywords to describe the scene.
4. The pupils dramatise the situation, practising it a few times. It need not be too rehearsed. The groups can then perform their scenes for the class.
5. The pupils assess their performance.
6. Still in groups, the pupils change the ending of a given rhyme.
7. All dramatisations can be discussed as a class.

Answers

1. – 7. Teacher check

Additional activities

Pupils can:

1. Discuss and act out scenes from historical events.
2. Act out parts of a class reading book.
3. Act out traditional stories/fairytales.
4. Complete written tasks based on dramas they have seen, either at the cinema, on television or in the classroom.

The ingredients for this lesson are imagination and drama!

1 Read the poem below with a group.

> It's raining cats and dogs!

Pitter-patter

Mothers grabbing their toddler's hands,
while others make a dash,
cars put on their headlights,
to avoid a slippery crash,
people running into shops,
though they've nothing to buy,
some grumbling and moaning,
about what falls from high,
cancelling plans to go to the beach,
being stuck indoors is a pain,
grabbing washing off the line,
c'mon, it's only rain!

> When the stars begin to huddle, the earth will soon become a puddle.

2 Imagine it is pouring with rain and you are somewhere outdoors. As a group, decide where you are:

_____

3 Think about this place in the rain. Write words to describe the scene in the box. Include how you feel about the rain.

4 Act out the scene. Rehearse it several times.

5 When you are ready, perform the scene for the class.

6 How was your performance? Rate it out of five by colouring one or more raindrops.

7 Write a new ending for this rhyme.

> *Rain, rain go away,*
> *Please come back another day.*

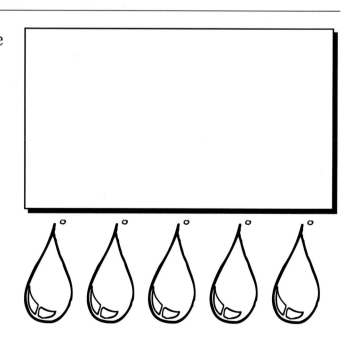

Rain, rain go away,

_____ .

Be an actor

Objective

React to poems through improvisational drama

Activities covered

- Reading a poem with a partner
- Acting out a poem
- Performing a poem
- Assessing performance
- Answering questions

Background information

This lesson gives pupils the opportunity to respond to what they have read through acting it out. The ideal place to practise their 'dramas' would be outside, where they cannot see or hear each other practising. The acting should be mostly ad lib. Pupils need to be supportive of each other, as acting in front of others can be difficult for shy pupils.

Before the lesson

The class will be divided into pairs.

The lesson

1. In pairs, pupils read the poem **'Wasting time'**. The teacher can read it first to the class and discuss any difficult words, such as 'lotions', 'sampled', 'potions' and 'trendy'. The poem should not be discussed as a class, this should be done in their pairs.

2. Pupils decide how they will act out the poem, writing their role on the poem. One person could be the mother and the other could be the child.

3. Pupils practise their poem, outside if possible.

4. Some pairs can perform the poem for the class.

5. Pupils assess their performance.

6. Still in groups, pupils answer questions about the poem, and discuss their own shopping experiences.

Answers

1. – 6. Teacher check

Additional activities

Pupils can:

1. Act out scenes from a class reader.

2. Act out TV programmes.

3. Act out well-known poems or stories such as Roald Dahl's **'Revolting rhymes'**.

You are going to respond to this poem by acting it out!

1 You are going to act out the poem in pairs. Think about how you will go about it as the teacher reads.

Wasting time

Mum said to me, 'We're going to the mall,
if you're very good, I'll buy you a leather ball'.

We seemed to walk for miles and miles,
I was grumpy and mum all smiles.

We looked at perfumes and colours for hair,
at skirts, at shirts, large underwear.

She tried on lipstick, gloss and blush,
she didn't seem in any rush.

She sought advice on creams for skin,
and potions that would make her thin.

She sampled lotions, paint for nails,
and tried on nightgowns meant for whales.

She browsed through rows of magazines,
and books on trendy fashion scenes.

And after visiting shops, so many,
she hardly parted with a penny.

We came home with a ball and bread,
the corner shop would have done instead!

Sound familiar?

2 Decide how you will act out this poem. Show your own role on the poem.

3 Practise acting out your poem.

4 Perform your poem for the class.

5 Assess your performance. Give yourselves a score out of 10 and write it in the star:

10

6 Answer these questions:

(a) Have you ever had a boring shopping experience?

☐ Yes ☐ No

(b) Where was it?

_____

(c) Tick on the poem the things you would find boring.

(d) What do you like shopping for?

_____

(e) What is your favourite shop?

_____

(f) How could the poet have made his/her time more interesting?

_____

_____

Make up your own

Objective

Write new versions of traditional nursery rhymes

Activities covered

- Reading a changed nursery rhyme
- Changing a rhyme with a partner
- Writing a rhyme
- Changing a rhyme
- Improving writing

Background information

Pupils need to experience the lighter side of language from time to time, whether it is reading funny poetry or telling jokes. The atmosphere for this lesson should be relaxed, with the pupils having fun with the words. The teacher should not worry too much about correct spelling and grammar in this lesson.

Recommended reading

(word play etc.)

The cheetah, my dearest, is known not to cheat by George Barker

Bees by Steve Turner

Where Mum drives me by Steve Turner

Body talk by Benjamin Zephaniah

On and on by Roger McGough

Down with flu by Matt Simpson

My job is by Gina Douthwaite

Jabberwocky by Lewis Carroll

Answer phone by John Mole

The Squirdle by Spike Milligan

On the Ning Nang Nong by Spike Milligan

Animal apologies by John Foster

Seasick by Nick Toczek

Before the lesson

Prepare a list of nursery rhymes the pupils can change.

The lesson

1. The pupils read the example of a changed rhyme.
2. The pupils work in pairs to change the rhyme **'Three blind mice'**.
3. The pupils choose a nursery rhyme and write it.
4. The pupils change the rhyme.
5. The pupils rewrite their rhyme, improving on it if they can.

Answers

1. – 6. Teacher check

Example: (Question 2):

> Three cute cats.
> Three cute cats.
> See how they chase. See how they chase.
> They all chase after a giant rat,
> They wanted to eat it. It was so fat.
> It went and hid under the hallway mat.
> Three cute cats.

Additional activities

Pupils can:

1. Hold a class joke-telling session, with each pupil having found a joke for homework the night before. Pupils can vote for the best joke.
2. Make up their own jokes.
3. Read humorous poetry and write similar poems.
4. Play games such as general knowledge, Pictionary®, Trivial Pursuit® or Balderdash®.

Websites

(jokes)

<www.ahajokes.com/kids_jokes.html>

<www.lotsofjokes.com/kids.htm>

We all know nursery rhymes. You are going to choose one and change it slightly, maybe even improve it!

1 Read the example below.

What do you get when you cross a poodle with a chicken? Pooched eggs!

> *Hey diddle diddle,*
> *The dog's done a widdle,*
> *Upon the new Persian mat,*
> *He will be put out,*
> *Of that there's no doubt,*
> *And be replaced by a house-trained cat.*

2 Find a partner to work with. Change the rhyme **'Three blind mice'** by adding in new words.

Three _____ _____

Three _____ _____

See how they _____ . See how they _____ .

They all _____

_____

_____

Three _____ _____ .

> Your rhyme should rhyme!

3 Choose another nursery rhyme and write it below.

4 On the nursery rhyme, change words or add ideas to make a new version.

5 Rewrite your new rhyme on a separate sheet of paper. Improve it if you can!

6 Display your completed rhyme in the classroom.

Objective

Extend and develop his/her response to increasingly challenging material

Activities covered

- Reading a poem
- Underlining words in a poem
- Writing word meanings
- Answering questions

Background information

At this age, pupils should be given increasingly challenging reading material. Reading should be fun, enjoyable and fulfilling; therefore it is vital that teachers choose reading material that is age-appropriate and interesting. Pupils should have a word book where they write all new words and their meanings. These books should be taken out when they are doing a written task.

Before the lesson

Provide examples of sentences using the words from Question 2.

The lesson

1. Read the poem *'Sabrina'* as a class.
2. The pupils underline the specified words in the poem and write their meanings, guessing if they do not know. The pupils should attempt this exercise on their own.
3. The pupils write who they think the nurse might be.
4. The pupils write down signs of the nurse's identity.
5. The pupils predict what might have happened after the poem ended.
6. All answers can be discussed as a class. The poem can also be reread and any other difficult words can be discussed. The class can use all new words in oral sentences.

Answers

1. Teacher check
2. (a) unable to move

   (b) giving/administering

   (c) not trusting

   (d) lady

   (e) easily broken/snapped

   (f) needed
3. a witch
4. deathly colour, possible wart on her chin, cackle, hooked nose, enjoys sweeping, lives in woods, black cat, pointed hat, night job etc.
5.–6. Teacher check

Additional activities

Pupils can:

1. Read challenging newspaper articles, poems, stories etc.
2. Have each pupil each cut a harder word from a magazine, and write the meaning and draw a picture to show the meaning. These can be displayed in the classroom.
3. Ensure the pupils read the written work of others on a frequent basis, so they can learn from each other.
4. Play games like Balderdash® or Pictionary® in groups.

Homework suggestion

Have the pupils look for five challenging words, and write down the meanings. Pupils bring them to class the following day and discuss or display them as appropriate.

Recommended reading

(witches)

Two witches discuss good grooming
by John Coldwell

Websites

(online dictionaries)

<www.thefreedictionary.com>

<www.webopedia.com>

Have you ever felt that somebody was familiar but you did not know who they were?
It happened to the boy in the poem below.

1 Read the poem.

Sabrina

I was lying in a hospital bed,
immobile and in pain.
I'd broken my arm on the trampoline,
Which was slippery from rain.

Now most of the nurses were friendly,
they laughed and smiled a lot.
They were even very gentle
when delivering a shot.

But one nurse was suspicious,
Sabrina was her name.
Her skin was a deathly colour,
She was a rather ugly dame.

She wore a plaster on her chin,
her hair was brittle and dry.
She cackled away all day long,
the sound nearly made me cry.

Her nose was hooked, her eyes were black,
she had a funny smell,
She seemed to enjoy sweeping,
And she did this rather well.

She said she lived out in the woods,
and owned a big, black cat.
She said she had a night job too,
that required a pointed hat.

She reminded me of someone,
though I couldn't think of
who.
It might come to me
later,
if I get another clue.

2 Underline these words in the poem and write their meanings.

(a) immobile _____

(b) delivering _____

(c) suspicious _____

(d) dame _____

(e) brittle _____

(f) required _____

3 Who do you think this nurse might be?

_____

4 Name some signs of her identity.

5 Discuss what may have happened after the poem ends.

6 Reread the poem!

Different tastes

Objective

Recognise and discuss differences in reading tastes

Activities covered

- Discussing different tastes
- Writing favourite things
- Discussing favourite things with a group
- Reading poems
- Discussing which poem is a favourite and why
- Discussing favourite books

Background information

It is important that pupils be allowed to pursue their own interests when it comes to reading. They should have the opportunity to choose their own reading material frequently. In this lesson, the pupils discuss different tastes generally and then different tastes in reading material.

Before the lesson

Divide the class into groups.

The lesson

1. Hold a class discussion about different tastes, in books, food, activities etc.
2. The pupils write their favourites for the headings listed in Question 1.
3. In groups, the pupils discuss their different tastes.
4. Still in groups, the pupils read the two poems. They should then discuss the poems. Each individual should tick which one he/she preferred and discuss why.
5. The pupils hold a group vote and circle the winning poem.
6. The pupils discuss in their groups their favourite type of books, and tick the appropriate boxes to complete Question 6.
7. The pupils work out which types of books are the most popular in their groups.

Answers

1. – 7. Teacher check

Additional activities

Pupils can:

1. Write book reviews and share them with the class.
2. Keep a list of the current TOP 10 books in the classroom.
3. Give a talk about something they have read.
4. Visit the library often so they can choose their own books.

We all have different tastes, in food, clothing, books, pastimes, TV programmes – in fact, in everything!

School is my favourite ....

1 Write down your favourite:

(a) sweet _____

(b) school subject _____

(c) song _____

(d) TV programme _____

(e) toy _____

2 In a small group, discuss your favourite things. Listen to what favourites others may have.

3 We can also have different tastes in reading. As a group, read both of these poems.

> (a) *My cat has met another cat,*
> *His name is Beastly Barry,*
> *It seems that they have fallen in love,*
> *And now they wish to marry.*

> (b) *Kitty,*
> *Fluffy, funny,*
> *Hunting, purring, snoozing,*
> *Bringing gifts of mice, rats and birds*
> *Fifi.*

4 Which poem do you prefer?   ☐ (a) ☐ (b)

5 Discuss why you prefer this poem with your group. Hold a group vote for the favourite poem. Circle the poem that won.

6 Discuss as a group what kind of books you like. Tick them. You can choose more than one type.

Science fiction...............	☐	True stories	☐
Humorous	☐	Mystery........................	☐
Nonfiction (fact)............	☐	Magazines	☐
Adventure	☐	Comics	☐
Horror	☐	Joke books...................	☐
Poetry	☐	Fantasy	☐

7 Which type of books are the most popular? _____

Discuss why. _____

Read aloud

Objective

Read aloud with expression

Activities covered

- Listening to teacher read
- Reading a poem with a partner
- Practising reading
- Using a checklist
- Writing a wish list

Background information

Pupils should be encouraged to always read with expression, although expression does not need to be overdone. Tone of voice, clarity, pronunciation, following punctuation marks and reading correctly are equally important aspects of reading. The teacher is the one who sets the standard of reading in the classroom.

Before the lesson

Divide the class into pairs.

The lesson

1. Read the poem **'What if … ?'** to the pupils. The class follows and listens. Point out pronunciation, correct words, clarity, expression, tone of voice etc.
2. With a partner, each pupil chooses a role (Mum or child) and the pairs read the poem together, concentrating on using expression. The mum would have a soothing voice and the child a worried tone for most of the poem.
3. The pupils practise reading the poem a few times, trying to improve their reading.
4. Using the checklist, the pupils assess their reading to answer Question 4.
5. The pupils write then read their Christmas or special occasion wish list. The pupils should be instructed to read their lists clearly, confidently and in a slightly pleading tone.

Answers

1. – 5. Teacher check

Additional activity

Pupils can:

Read the following with expression: parts of a class reader, short plays, other poems, song words, a speech they have written, a dialogue, own writing.

Homework suggestion

Provide each pupil with a piece to read aloud to a family member.

Recommended reading

(Christmas)

Mother Christmas's demands
by Andrea Shavick

Out of season by Paul Cookson

The day after the day after Boxing Day
by Paul Cookson

The wrong words by Brian Moses

Dear Father Christmas by Roger Stevens

Blue Christmas by Adrian Henri

Christmas thank you's by Mick Gowar

Websites

(stories)

<www.magickeys.com>
<www.childrenstoryhour.com>

Reading aloud does not mean reading loudly!
When reading aloud, speak clearly and slowly, and always use expression.

1 Listen to the teacher read the poem below. Take note of the expression he/she uses.

> Reading is to the mind what exercise is to the body.

What if … ?

Child	'Mum, what if on this Christmas Eve, Santa forgets to come here?'
Mum	'Santa remembers every child, and that includes you, dear.'
Child	'Mum, what if Santa's stuck in a chimney, because he's got too fat?'
Mum	'His reindeer will then rescue him, they're very used to that.'
Child	'Mum, what if Santa comes tonight, and I'm still wide awake?'
Mum	'I suspect he'll come back later, but sleep now for goodness sake!'
Child	'Mum, what if Santa's worn-out sleigh, gets tired and breaks down?'
Mum	'He has a fleet of back-ups, hidden in every town.'
Child	'Mum, what if Santa doesn't think, that I've been good at all?'
Mum	'But you've been a wonderful child, so I know that he will call.'
Child	'Mum, what if Santa didn't get, the wish list I sent today? I completely changed my mind, you see, But I know it will be OK!'
Child	'Mum, are you all right?'

> I hope there is a book on this list!

2 Read the poem with a partner, using expression and the right tone of voice! One person should be the child and the other should be the mum.

3 Practise the poem a few times.

4 Use the checklist to show how well you read the poem.

Clear voice......................	☐
Expression......................	☐
Tone of voice.................	☐
No stumbling	☐
Correct words................	☐
Pronunciation	☐

5 What do you wish for this Christmas or special occasion? Write it down and read it to your partner.

_____

_____

_____

_____

Objective

Write about experiences and feelings in diary form

Activities covered

- Reading a poem
- Writing a diary entry
- Writing about today – keywords
- Writing a diary entry for the day

Background information

This exercise allows pupils to reflect on their experiences and put them into writing. Diary entries are usually personal and therefore pupils should not have to share what they have written with the teacher or classmates. The teacher will obviously have to check that the exercise is done, but it is not necessary to read it thoroughly. Diary entries should not only contain the experiences of the writer, but feelings or worries he/she might have had.

Before the lesson

Prepare examples of diary entries; e.g. Anne Frank's diary.

The lesson

1. Read the poem *'What the … ?'* as a class.

2. The pupils write a diary entry for the person in the poem. They need not write what was said, only what events occurred.

3. The pupils write keywords for their own diary entry. Inform pupils that they will not have to share their writing with anyone. This should allow them more freedom with their writing.

4. The pupils write a diary entry for their day so far, including experiences and any feelings they may have had. The pupils do not need to share their diaries with anyone.

Answers

1. – 4. Teacher check

Additional activities

Pupils can:

1. Look at other diary entries; e.g. Anne Frank's diary, <www.annefrank.com> or <www.annefrank.org>

2. Convert parts of the following into diary entries: class reader, TV programme, film, newspaper article.

3. Write diary entries pretending to be a cat/tree/teacher/mobile phone etc.

Homework suggestion

Have the pupils keep a diary for a week. After this time, they could discuss what it was like to keep a diary.

Recommended reading

The warthog's diary by Marian Swinger
Diary of Jack, Diary of Jill by Peter Dixon

A diary is a daily record of experiences and feelings.

1 Read the poem below as a class.

What the … .?

What the … ?

Have you ever noticed,
We don't always speak well?
We can often stop midair,
Without finishing to tell.

When Mum saw muddy footprints,
All across the hall,
And even quite a few of them,
Going up the wall,
She said, 'What the … ?'

When Dad looked out the window,
At the wet and muddy lawn,
With quad bike tracks right through it,
The grass all ripped and torn,
He said, 'What the … ?'

When Teacher saw my project,
On which I'd spilt my eggs and ham,
You could really read the most of it,
If it wasn't for the jam,
She said, 'What the … ?'

When my neighbour saw me running,
Through the garden almost bare,
I was really hot you see,
So I just had underwear,
He said, 'What the … ?'

When I was grounded, by my mum,
And my dad called me a pest,
The teacher threw my project back,
And I was under arrest,
I said, 'What the … ?'

2 Imagine you were this person. Write one or two of his/her diary entries for the day.

Use full sentences.

Dear diary _____

_____
_____
_____
_____
_____
_____
_____
_____
_____
_____
_____
_____

3 Write keywords for your diary entry for today. Include the experiences you had and your feelings.

4 Write your diary entry in full on a sheet of paper.

Objective

Create limericks

Activities covered

- Reading a limerick
- Completing limericks
- Writing own limerick
- Assessing own limerick

Background information

Limericks rely heavily on the number of syllables in each line. However, the pupils should not get too bogged down with this. The important thing is that the limerick has the correct rhythm – if a line is one or two syllables short, it does not matter. The rhyme scheme is also important and should be adhered to. The teacher should go through the example given, and perhaps Question 1 (a) can be done together as a class. The pupils then have practice before writing their own.

Before the lesson

Pupils will need to have some knowledge of syllables and how words are broken up before they are able to do this lesson.

The lesson

1. Explain to the pupils how a limerick is written. This is done using the example provided, making reference to the syllables, rhythm and rhyme scheme.
2. The pupils complete two limericks. The first can be done as a class.
3. The pupils write and assess their own limerick.

Answers

1. (a) example: Spain, play, swim, mane

   (b) example: kitty, Chad, make other cats mad, picked many fights, On long winter nights, now lives alone and is sad.

2. – 3. Teacher check

Additional activities

Pupils can:

1. Write stories, verses, haiku, cinquains, tankas etc.
2. Complete a writing assignment—e.g. a four-line poem—using a topic from another learning area.
3. Look at paintings and write stories or paragraphs based on them.
4. Change well-known fairytales by changing one of the characters, or part of the plot etc.
5. Write a story as a class or group.

Websites

<www.loonylimericks.com>
<www.poetry-online.org/limericks.htm>
(These are for the teacher to get ideas from.)

A limerick is a type of humorous poem. An example is given below.

It is five lines long:

1st line – 7 to 10 syllables ——— ***There once was a boy in my school,***

2nd line – 7 to 10 syllables ——— ***Who thought himself very cool,***

3rd line – 5 to 7 syllables ——— ***His hair was dyed blue,***

4th line – 5 to 7 syllables ——— ***And spiked up with goo,***

5th line – 7 to 10 syllables ——— ***In fact, he looked just like a fool.***

Lines 1, 2 and 5 rhyme.   Lines 3 and 4 rhyme.

1 Use the format above to complete the limericks below.

(a)   There once was a lion from _____ ,

Who loved to _____ in the rain.

In the puddles he'd _____ ,

No-one could stop him,

Took him ages to blow-dry his _____ .

(b)   There once was a _____ from _____ ,

Who loved to _____ ,

He _____ ,

_____ ,

He _____ .

2 Try to write your own limerick. You may like to draft it on a separate sheet of paper first.

_____

_____

_____

_____

_____

3 Give your limerick a score out of 5.

What is your reaction?

Objective

Express in writing his/her reactions to poems

Activities covered

- Writing possible reactions to different situations
- Discussing reactions
- Reading a poem
- Writing a reaction to poem
- Writing reactions shown in other situations

Background information

For this lesson, choose reading material that will evoke some reaction in the pupils. The pupils need to be able to record their own reactions.

Before the lesson

Prepare examples of poetry that is likely to cause the pupils to have a reaction.

The lesson

1. Discuss the word 'reaction' with the class. The pupils can give examples of different reactions. 'Reaction' means a response that we have to something/someone. A reaction usually shows feelings and attitudes.
2. The pupils write what they would say in the three different situations given in Question 1. They should use full sentences.
3. The pupils discuss their answers to Question 1 with the class.
4. Read the poem *'Stew won't do'* as a class. Discuss more difficult words such as 'loathe' and 'create'.
5. The pupils write their reaction to the poem, using full sentences.
6. The pupils comment on how they feel about stew, using full sentences.
7. The pupils write one food they particularly dislike and how they would react if they were served this food.

Answers

1. – 6. Teacher check

Additional activities

Pupils can:

1. Read a poem and write to the poet describing their reaction to the poem.
2. Read a poem and write a review or draw their reactions.

Homework suggestion

Have the pupils read *'Stew won't do'* to a member of their family and record his/her reaction.

Recommended reading

Nothing tastes quite like a gerbil
by Tony Langham

Watch it by John Coldwell

Food for thought by Michaela Morgan

Think of all the poor pupils by Steve Turner

Horace by Terry Jones

The taste exchanger by Alison Chisholm

Talking turkeys by Benjamin Zephaniah

We have many different reactions during a day. What sort of reaction do you have when the teacher gives you heaps of homework?

1 What would you say in the following situations?

(a) You have to stay with a grumpy relative all weekend.

'_____'

(b) You win £250 in an art competition.

'_____'

(c) While you are playing outside, a spaceship flies above your head.

'_____'

2 Discuss different reactions with your class.

> A reaction is how you respond to something.

3 Read the poem below as a class.

4 Give your reaction to this poem.

_____

_____

_____

Stew won't do

My Dad's favourite meal,
is home-cooked stew.
But we all loathe it,
it's like eating goo.

Now, as far as stews go,
I think the idea's great,
a mish-mash of food,
piled up on your plate.

But instead of the veggies,
the lamb and the rice,
Couldn't we create something,
tasty and nice?

A stew made of marshmallows,
chocolates and nuts,
would bring children running,
to sit on their butts.

At the dining room table,
they'd be asking for more.
And Dad's boring old dish
would have gone out the door.

> Irish stew in Irish is *stobhach gaelach.*

5 Do you feel the same way about stew? Explain in a full sentence.

_____

_____

_____

6 (a) Name a food that you really do not like.

_____

(b) Explain how you would react if you were served this food in a fancy restaurant.

_____

_____

_____

Draw then write

Objective

Use his/her own artwork and that of others as a stimulus to writing

Activities covered

- Looking at artwork
- Reading a poem with a given format
- Writing a poem with a given format
- Reading a poem to self
- Assessing own poem and artwork
- Adding title to artwork

Background information

The pupils write about their own artwork in this lesson. The teacher should encourage pupils to be descriptive and make their poems as interesting as possible. The poem pupils will write is about one particular colour, so this must be the focus of their artwork. Soft classical music in the background will provide the right mood when doing the artwork and writing the poem. The music for both activities should be the same.

Before the lesson

The pupils will need to have completed a work of art for this lesson (see 'Background information'). The artwork should be predominantly in one colour of their choice; for example, if they have chosen red, their artwork should be full of things that are red, such as tomatoes, apples, ketchup or cherries.

The lesson

1. Read the format of the poem provided. An example can be done together as a class (see below).
2. The pupils look at their artwork. There should be silence in the classroom at this time so that they can concentrate.
3. The pupils write a poem about their artwork, using the 'formula' on the copymaster.
4. The pupils read their poem to themselves and assess their artwork and poem.
5. The pupils give their artwork a title. They can then cut out their poem and display it with their artwork.

Answers

1. – 5. Teacher check

Additional activities

Pupils can:

1. Use their own artwork as a stimulus when writing stories, captions, poems etc.
2. Look at famous paintings and write a story/poem.
3. Write captions for their own works of art.

Example:

Green, green, hello green,
Welcome to a lush farm field.
Green, green, let's scream for green!
Chestnut leaves,
Sweet damp grass,
Slippery moss on the path,
Weeds choking the beauty,
Slimy water in a still pond,
Yeah! Let's hear it for green!

1 Take some time to look at a piece of art you have created.

2 Write a poem about it using the format below.

> A picture is worth a thousand words.

colour _____ , *colour* _____ , hello *colour* _____ !

Welcome to *something that colour* _____

colour _____ , *colour* _____ , let's *verb* _____ for *colour* _____ .

two things that colour _____ , _____ ,

two things that colour _____ , _____ ,

something that colour - phrase _____

something that colour - phrase _____

Yeah! Let's hear it for *colour* _____ !

> Your poem should match your picture!

_____ , _____ , hello _____ !

Welcome to _____

_____ , _____ , let's _____ for _____ .

_____ , _____ ,

_____ , _____ ,

_____

_____

Yeah! Let's hear it for _____ !

3 Read your poem to yourself.
Score your poem and artwork.

ART ___/5

POEM ___/5

4 Give your artwork a title.

_____

_____

5 Display your artwork and poem together.

> Xanthic is a yellowish colour.